AN

NMR PRIMER

FOR LIFE SCIENTISTS

HENRY RATTLE

AN

NMR PRIMER

FOR LIFE SCIENTISTS

PARTNERSHIP PRESS 1995

First published in Great Britain in 1995 by

Partnership Press
P.O.Box 102 Fareham Hants PO16 7YB

ISBN 0-9516436-3-0 (Pbk)

Acknowledgements

The author wishes to thank the following for advice, assistance and permission to reproduce diagrams: Bruker Spectrospin Ltd.; Dr. Marius Clore; Dr.Peter Cary; Dr.Tony Ferrige; Surgeon Commander Jeremy Hogg, RN; Dr.Chris Read; Dr.Derek Shaw; Siemens plc Medical Engineering; Chris Turner.
He also owes a debt to the students of Molecular Biology at the University of Portsmouth for whom these lecture notes were originally written, and to the authors of the many books and review articles which have been consulted during the preparation of the manuscript. Any errors or omissions remain his responsibility alone, and will of course be corrected in any future printings in the light of comments received.

Contents

PREFACE

Nuclear Magnetic Resonance, with its applications in biochemistry
and medicine, is a vast subject. Libraries of texts are published
about it, and they are often expensive and heavily mathematical.
This book has been written to provide life science students with an
accessible and affordable introduction which, using pictorial vector
descriptions rather than the mathematics of a quantum-mechanical
treatment, introduces the ideas of NMR to the point where journal
articles describing biochemical and medical applications should be
understandable. The basic principles are straightforward, at least in
the sense that ideas become straightforward when other people
have thought of them first, and I hope that readers will find themselves able to follow those presented here fairly readily. Of course, a
primer is simply an introductory text, a first look, a small book of
elementary principles; the aim is therefore not to be comprehensive,
but rather to be comprehensible to a first-time reader. Once you
want to go beyond this, to design your own experiments or to
operate an NMR spectrometer, quite a lot of further reading will be
needed, and the select bibliography at the end of this book suggests
some excellent next steps.

HWR December 1994

CHAPTER 1: FOUNDATION IDEAS

Being some general principles that are important in NMR

A billiard ball – the classic "classical entity"

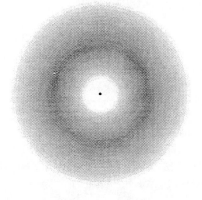

Attempt to indicate the "fuzzy" nature of a quantum-mechanical entity such as an atom.

1.1 Pictures of reality

The world of atoms and molecules is only indirectly accessible from the macroscopic world of everyday experience, and must thus be described and handled by using analogies. The two most powerful pictures that we have are the classical and the quantum-mechanical. Both of these are properly treated using mathematics, but the classical picture also provides reasonable mental images because the familiar everyday world operates largely on classical laws. In the classical picture nuclei, atoms, and molecules are regarded as obeying Newton's laws in much the same way as large objects such as billiard balls, with exactly defined physical properties such as position and momentum. (The billiard ball has for many years been used as the prime example of a well-behaved macroscopic object with totally predictable properties – the author's experience with billiard balls does not entirely support this assumption). The energy and momentum of classical objects are allowed to take any values, with no restrictions. Classical theory can be very successful (for example, in the form of the kinetic theory of gases and heat) but the classical picture fails in important ways when trying to predict the details of atomic and molecular structure and behaviour. Quantum mechanics (which provides us with a mathematical description in terms of the Schrodinger equation or of a matrix-based method devised by Dirac) is much more satisfactory. In principle at least, it can explain all the observable properties of atoms or molecules; finding actual solutions for specific cases, especially those involving more than a very few atoms, is often extremely difficult.

The mathematical nature of quantum mechanics means that there are often no readily accessible mental images to go with the solution to a quantum-mechanical equation. A quantum object is described in terms of probabilities, which means that any attempt to depict it runs into problems – how do you imagine or draw a probability? The quantum-mechanical description of a system further requires that each of its observable properties, such as energy or momentum, is restricted to a set of fixed values characteristic of the system, and that they are never found with values between these fixed ones. The observable properties are said to be *quantised*.

In discussing NMR, it is convenient to make use of both classical and quantum-mechanical approaches. It can be helpful to describe atomic nuclei as if they behave like large objects such as gyroscopes or bar magnets, while accepting that the only really accurate way of describing them is mathematical. To understand and apply NMR fully it is necessary to use quantum-mechanical formalisms, but the classical picture is the one that most people work with more readily, and it is adequate to follow most of the literature describing applications of NMR. In this primer for life scientists we confine our discussions almost entirely to a non-mathematical classical formalism. This will mean sometimes having to state a result without justifying it; readers wishing for a full mathematical approach are referred to the excellent books which use and explain the appropriate quantum mechanics and are listed in the bibliography at the back of the book.

1.2 Magnetism

The proton, electron and neutron which are the basic sub-atomic particles each exhibit a number of intrinsic properties, one of the most important being charge. The evidence for the presence of charge is the force that one stationary charged particle exerts on another – attractive for oppositely charged particles, repulsive for like charges, and varying inversely with the square of the distance between them. Such electrostatic forces are very strong, and of course are responsible for all atomic and molecular structure and interactions. In themselves, electrostatic forces play little part in life at the macroscopic level, because positive and negative charge are normally precisely balanced.

When a charge is moving, however, a new phenomenon appears. The moving charge gives rise to a *magnetic field*, which appears through the effect of motion on the electrostatic forces. A magnetic field has the property that an electric charge moving through it will experience a force. It is usual to define the strength of magnetic fields in terms of *magnetic flux density* B; the unit of B is the *tesla*. Since a magnetic field has direction as well as intensity, B is a vector quantity. A magnetic field is usefully depicted in diagrams by "lines of force" which follow the direction of the field; lines of force are closer together in regions of stronger field.

Magnetic fields are only produced by moving charges. This is true even in the case of so-called permanent magnets, where the magnetic effect is produced by the concerted motion of electrons within

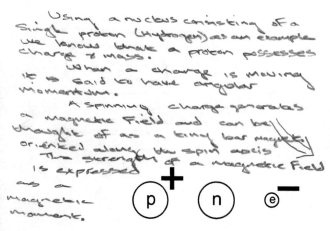

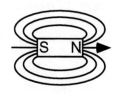

Lines of force from a bar magnet.

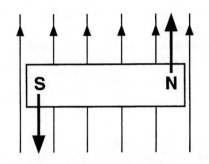

Magnetic Moment – the turning force in a one-tesla field.

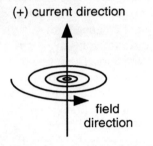

Field produced by a current in a wire.

the atoms of the magnetic material. The idea of a permanent magnet, a bar of material producing a magnetic field and having "North" (North-seeking in the Earth's magnetic field) and "South" poles, leads us to two useful definitions. If a permanent magnet is placed at right angles to a uniform magnetic field, it will experience a turning force or couple. If the strength of the field is one tesla, the strength of this couple is called the *magnetic moment* m of the magnet. This leads to a further definition: inside a magnetised material, the *intensity of magnetisation* M is the magnetic moment per unit volume of the material.

The commonest example of moving charge is a current flowing in a wire. If the current (conventionally a flow of positive charge, even though current in a metal is in fact the motion of negatively-charged electrons) flows along a straight wire, the direction of the magnetic field is around the wire as indicated in the diagram.

Box 1.1: The Units of Magnetism

Magnetic effects are only produced by moving charges, and they are only experienced by moving charges. This leads to two different (but closely related, of course) ways of defining the units in which magnetic fields are measured.

If we are considering the magnetic effects *produced by* a moving charge, we define the *magnetic intensity* H. This is related to the magnetic field produced by the flow of an electric current I in a wire, and is defined by Ampere's theorem: if the length of wire is ds, then the magnetic intensity H at point P defined as shown in the diagram at right is

$$H = I \, ds \sin \theta \, / \, 4\pi r^2.$$

The units of H are amperes per metre (Am^{-1}) and the direction of H in this diagram is into the page.

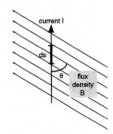

The alternative way of defining a magnetic field is to do it in terms of the force *experienced by* a moving charge. The force F on a current element consisting of a current I moving along a piece of wire length ds in a magnetic field is defined as:

$$F = B \, I \, ds \cos \theta$$

where B is the *magnetic flux density* at that point. In the diagram at left, the force F would be out of the paper. The unit of B is the tesla (T).

Of course, magnetic intensity H and magnetic flux density B are intimately related. The relationship takes the form of a constant μ_o, where μ_o is called the permeability of free space, and has the value $4\pi \times 10^{-7}$ henry per metre. Thus $B = \mu_o H$.

The natural magnetic field of Earth, which causes compass needles to point North, has a flux density in the region of 50 microtesla, varying from place to place. The magnets used for NMR produce flux density millions of times stronger, ranging between 0.3 tesla for a low-field imaging magnet to about 18 tesla for the highest-field superconducting magnet currently manufactured for NMR use.

You may find when reading older papers that magnetic field strengths are quoted in *gauss*. In this case it is useful to know that one tesla is equivalent to 10,000 gauss.

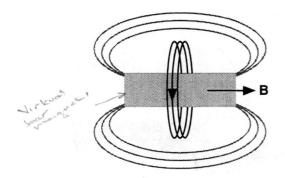

Magnetic effect of current in a coil.

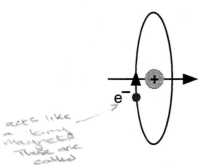

Magnetic effect of circulating electron in a paramagnetic atom.

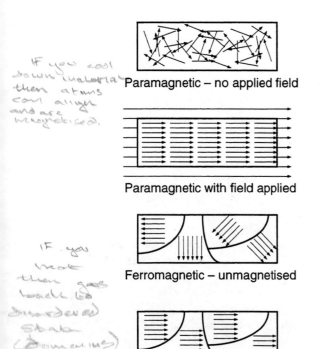

Paramagnetic – no applied field

Paramagnetic with field applied

Ferromagnetic – unmagnetised

Ferromagnetic – magnetised

Schematic diagrams of magnetic materials.

If the wire is bent into a coil, the magnetic fields produced by each segment of the wire add so as to produce a pattern very similar to that produced by a bar magnet. Thus a coil of wire carrying an electric current can have a magnetic moment in exactly the same way as a bar magnet.

1.3 Magnetic materials

Magnetic effects are produced by all currents; since the motion of an electron orbiting the nucleus of an atom also represents a current, the atom may produce a local magnetic field. In doing so it becomes in itself a small permanent magnet, with its own magnetic moment. In most stable atoms and molecules the electrons are paired so that these magnetic effects cancel and are not observed; in a few, however, there are unpaired electrons; each atom or molecule then acts as a small magnet and will tend to align itself along an externally-applied magnetic field B_{app}. Such materials are called *paramagnetic*. Since the alignment of the atomic magnets is generally along the applied field, the magnetic effects of the atoms add to that of the field so that B_{ins} inside the material is greater than the applied B_{app}. The relation between the two is given by $B_{ins}=\kappa B_{app}$, where κ, the *relative permeability constant*, is greater than 1. As soon as the external magnetic field is removed, of course, the induced magnetisation dies away as thermal motions disorder the atomic magnets again.

Of course the atoms of a paramagnetic material, each acting as a magnet, do have a natural tendency to line up with each other – not just when an external field is applied, but all the time. The interaction is usually weak, and thermal energies in the material prevent alignment actually taking place. In a few cases, though, the energy of interaction is great enough to overcome the effects of thermal agitation at normal temperatures. The individual atomic magnetic moments then stay in alignment with each other, their individual magnetic moments adding to produce a large total magnetic moment. Materials exhibiting this property are called *ferromagnetic*, and are used to make permanent magnets. In practice, the regions of fully aligned atomic moments in a ferromagnetic material are quite small (they are called domains) and don't naturally align with each other: a piece of, say, iron will only exhibit the properties of a permanent magnet if the domains within it can be persuaded to line up. The process of aligning the domains, for example by placing a piece of iron in a strong magnetic field, is what happens when we magnetise a piece of iron.

The last type of magnetic material which is appropriate to mention here is the *superparamagnetic*. This term is applied to finely-divided materials which have aligned magnetic moments within individual particles, rather like the individual domains of a ferromagnetic. In the presence of a magnetic field, the particles, suspended in a

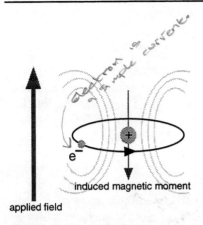

The diamagnetic effect – applied magnetic field induces opposing magnetic moment in each atom.

induced mag. field in
opposite direction
to applied mag. field

liquid, can align to give a very strong paramagnetic effect; as soon as the magnetic field is removed, thermal motions mean that the magnetisation soon decays to zero. Superparamagnetics are sometimes used as contrast agents in magnetic resonance imaging (see Chapter 7).

Finally we may note that the forces experienced by a charged particle moving through a region of magnetic field are also experienced if the charge is stationary and the field is moving: thus a current may be induced to flow in a wire placed in a region of changing magnetic field (*electromagnetic induction*). In the same way the application of a magnetic field to any sample of atoms or molecules may be considered to induce currents by altering the orbital motions of their electrons. This is the *diamagnetic effect* and it is common to all materials, whether or not they are paramagnetic or ferromagnetic as well. Currents induced in this way produce their own magnetic fields; if molecular orientations are not restricted this induced magnetisation of the atoms or molecules will be in the opposite direction to the applied field. Diamagnetic materials have values of κ less than unity – the field inside them is weaker than the applied field because of the induced atomic magnets. Diamagnetic effects are much smaller than paramagnetic effects, but because they are common to all atoms and molecules they play an important role in NMR.

1.4 Electromagnetic radiation.

Electrostatic and magnetic interactions are intimately associated with electromagnetic radiation, and any form of spectroscopy (of which magnetic resonance is an example) depends on the interaction of atoms or molecules with radiation in some region of the electromagnetic spectrum. A *classical* description of electromagnetic radiation regards it as a wavelike variation of electric field propagating through space with velocity $c=3 \times 10^8$ metres per second and having frequency ν and wavelength λ related by $c=\nu\lambda$. Associated with the electric field variation is a varying magnetic field perpendicular to it; it is this component that is most important in the classical view of NMR. The *quantum* view of electromagnetic radiation describes it in terms of packets or quanta of energy $h\nu$, where h is Planck's constant and has a value of 6.626×10^{-34} joule seconds. The radiation used for NMR has frequencies in the range 10^6-10^9 Hz (1-1000 MHz). This falls in the *radiofrequency* region of the spectrum, with longer wavelengths and lower energies than visible light. For example, radiation of frequency 100 MHz (about the frequency of FM radio) has a wavelength of 3 metres and a quantum energy of about 10^{-25} joules. Visible light is around ten million times smaller in wavelength, and thus ten million times greater in frequency and energy.

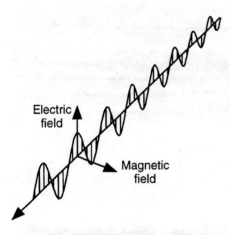

Electromagnetic radiation: a varying electric field, with a varying magnetic field perpendicular to it, and all travelling at speed c.

1.5 Energy in molecules

Atomic or molecular systems may possess energy in a number of different forms. Some is associated with the translational, rotational and vibrational motions of the molecules, some with the interactions between electrons and nuclei. The common feature shared by all these forms of energy is that they are *quantised* – each form of energy, separately, is restricted to certain values (energy levels). For any particular type of energy, the gaps between allowed levels depend on the nature of the system and are characteristic of it, so that measurement of energy gaps in atoms and molecules is one of the most important ways of testing models of their structure.

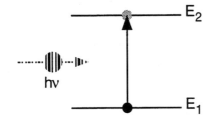

Transition between energy levels E_1 and E_2 induced by a photon of energy $h\nu$ where $h\nu=E_2-E_1$.

Electromagnetic radiation can interact with molecules or atoms to cause transitions between allowed energy states. This occurs when the energy of a photon of the radiation, given by $E=h\nu$ where ν is the frequency of the radiation and h is Planck's constant, is exactly equal to the energy gap between the states. This phenomenon forms the basis of all types of spectroscopy, with different regions of the electromagnetic spectrum corresponding to different energy regimes in the system; for example, ultraviolet radiation corresponds to electronic energy gaps in molecules and infrared to molecular vibrational energies.

The general scheme of a spectroscopic experiment is that the system, with the populations of its energy levels initially determined by the Boltzmann distribution (see below) is irradiated using a range of wavelengths within the appropriate region of the spectrum. Interactions between radiation and sample then result in the promotion of some molecules or atoms to higher energy levels, with an absorption of energy at the corresponding wavelength from the radiation. Analysis of the radiation emerging from the sample reveals the missing wavelengths and hence the energy gaps present in the sample. The amount of radiation absorbed depends on a number of factors, including the amount of sample present and a 'transition probability' stemming from the precise nature of the interaction between radiation and molecule. It is also possible for molecules or atoms which are already in an excited state to be stimulated by the incident radiation into a downward transition, with consequent emission of another photon of the same energy: systems capable of this type of emission form the basis of lasers, but the effect is also important in NMR.

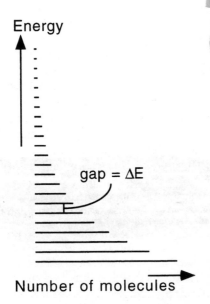

The Boltzmann distribution – higher energy levels have smaller populations.

In addition to the spacing of energy levels for a system, we must also consider their occupancy when the system is at equilibrium: how are the molecules of the sample distributed among the available energy states? The key factor here is the relation between the energy of each state and the available thermal energy (measured in units of kT where k is Boltzmann's constant and T the absolute temperature). The distribution is then described by the *Boltzmann relation*. If two states e1 (with a population of $\eta 1$) and e2 (with a population of η2) are separated by an energy gap ΔE (where ΔE, of course, equals e2 – e1), the ratio of their populations is given by η1/η2= exp(-ΔE/kT).

This relation tells us that if ΔE is large compared to kT, very few molecules are in the upper state compared to the lower; such is the case for the electronic energy levels of molecules, where the populations of any states above the lowest (ground state) energy may be assumed to be negligible at normal temperatures. On the other hand, when ΔE is small, (which is the case in NMR) the ratio of populations tends towards unity, so that upper and lower states are almost, but not quite, equally populated. Exactly equal populations are never found in practice for a system at equilibrium; they would only occur if the energy gap between the states were zero, or the temperature infinite.

1.6 Angular momentum and spin

In classical mechanics a body of mass m and velocity v possesses a *linear momentum* mv. Since velocity is a vector quantity, defined in both magnitude and direction, momentum is also a vector. Linear momentum is conserved during elastic collisions and other changes to a system. These ideas about linear momentum have parallels for rotational motion. If a body is rotating with an angular velocity ω radians per second, it has an *angular momentum* Iω, where I, the moment of inertia of the body, depends on the mass of the body and its shape relative to the axis about which it rotates. Like linear momentum, angular momentum is a vector quantity, and is conveniently represented by an arrow directed along the axis of rotation and of length proportional to the magnitude of the angular momentum.

Classical mechanics places no limits on either the magnitude or the direction of angular momentum, but a quantum mechanical treatment of the angular momentum of, say, an orbiting electron shows it to be quantised. Further, the quantisation applies to both the magnitude *and the direction* of the angular momentum vector. The magnitude of the angular momentum of any rotating body or system is restricted to values related to the *angular momentum quantum number* j, where j is 0 or a positive integer or half-integer 1/2, 1, 3/2, 2, 5/2.... The direction of the angular momentum vector is specified relative to one direction in space, and in this direction it is restricted to values nh/2π, where n has values j, j–1, j–2 .... 0, ...– j. (This phenomenon is called *space quantisation*). The result of these two restrictions is that the axis of the spinning system will always be found in one of (2j+1) orientations in space. If j=1/2, *only two orientations will be allowed*, as in the diagram at left. Because of the very small value of h, none of these restrictions of magnitude or direction are observable for macroscopic objects, but they are dominant in systems on an atomic scale.

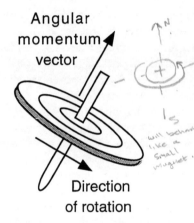

Angular momentum vector of a spinning top.

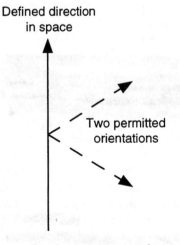

The angular momentum vector for a particle with j=1/2 must be in one of two directions in space.

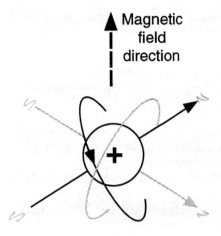

The two permitted orientations for the angular momentum vector of a nucleus with I=1/2 in a magnetic field. The orientations have slightly different energies.

one is in a higher energy state than the other?

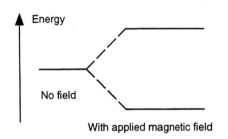

Splitting of energy state of nucleus by applied magnetic field.

On an atomic scale, it is not only orbiting electrons that exhibit quantised angular momentum; isolated particles, both electrons and nuclei, also possess it. Since this angular momentum may conveniently, if inaccurately, be regarded as resulting from the rotation of the particle about its own axis, it is termed *spin*. The spin of a particle is a fixed property, like its charge. Electrons have a spin angular momentum quantum number, s, of $1/2$, as do isolated protons and neutrons; the spin quantum number, I, of more complex particles such as the nucleus of an atom may be integral or half-integral. Most NMR experiments are performed on nuclei having I = $1/2$, a class which includes the most abundant isotopes of hydrogen, fluorine and phosphorus as well as carbon-13 and nitrogen-15. Spin angular momentum obeys the rules governing magnitude and direction outlined above, so that these spin -$1/2$ particles are restricted to two orientations relative to a fixed direction in space; more generally, a nucleus with spin quantum number I will be found in one of (2I+1) orientations.

Our picture of the atomic nucleus as a charged object spinning about an axis provides a basis for understanding, at least at a superficial level, its interaction with a magnetic field. Just like an orbiting electron, a spinning charged particle (electron or nucleus) may be regarded as a tiny loop current with its own associated magnetic moment. The lowest energy state of such a magnet is reached when it is aligned along an applied field; however, our elementary magnet is subject to the rules of space quantisation, and can take up only (2I+1) orientations. Because each of these is oriented differently with respect to the applied field, each will have a different energy, and so the effect of a magnetic field on the particle is to split its energy into (2I+1) separate levels. The energy gaps between these levels are very small: thus their populations at equilibrium, given by the Boltzmann distribution, are nearly equal.

1.7 Precessional motion

As we have just seen, the application of a magnetic field to a spinning charged nucleus splits its energy into a number of different levels. It also causes an effect which may be regarded classically as a *precession* of the nucleus about the direction of the field. Precessional motion is the kind shown by a gyroscope spinning in the gravitational field of earth: the axis about which the gyroscope spins is itself rotating about the vertical. In gyroscopes, the effect arises from the interaction between the angular momentum vector of the gyroscope and the force of gravity. Our spinning nucleus also has angular momentum, and this can interact with an applied magnetic field via its own magnetic moment. The precessional motion of a nucleus occurs at a rate called its LARMOR FREQUENCY which depends on the type of nucleus (i.e. the precise number of protons and neutrons which make it up) and is directly proportional to the strength of the applied field.

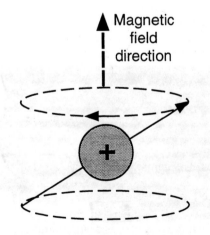

Precessional motion of a charged spinning nucleus in a magnetic field.

Excitation and relaxation.

1.8 Excited states and relaxation

The absorption of electromagnetic radiation leaves a population of atoms or molecules in an *excited state;* that is, the distribution of molecules among the available energy states is perturbed from the equilibrium (Boltzmann) situation. The atoms or molecules will tend to return spontaneously to their equilibrium state over a period of time; this process is known as *relaxation*. The probability of a spontaneous transition is proportional to the cube of the transition energy, and this only becomes significant for relatively high energies, for transitions with energies in the ultraviolet spectroscopic region and above. For the very small energy gaps associated with NMR, relaxation is not spontaneous but must be induced by some process within the sample. The time taken for a given perturbed system to relax back to equilibrium will depend on the nature of these "relaxation mechanisms" and will yield information about motions and interactions within the sample.

The relaxation time has another significance; it is a consequence of the Uncertainty Principle of Heisenberg that the energy of a state which is occupied for a time t is uncertain by δE ,where the product of δE and t is greater than $h/2\pi$. Thus if relaxation takes place very fast, (i.e. the perturbed state is occupied for a very short time, and t is small), δE will be large and there will be a measurable uncertainty in the energy of the transition (as measured by the frequency of the radiation emitted or absorbed). If we plot the energy of the transition on a graph, it will not appear as a single line at a fixed energy, but as a band of energies with a finite linewidth. The shorter the lifetime, the broader the line. We will return to this concept in Chapter Two.

1.9 One view of the NMR experiment

The basic NMR experiment may thus be seen as follows: an *atomic nucleus* which has an *angular momentum quantum number* I and an associated nuclear *magnetic moment* is restricted by *space quantisation* rules to (2I+1) orientations in space. Normally these orientations are *degenerate* (have the same energy as each other), but application of a magnetic field B causes their energy to split into (2I+1) separate levels with small *energy gaps* between them. At equilibrium the populations of these levels are not quite equal, with slightly more nuclei in the lower energy states. Application of electromagnetic radiation in the appropriate frequency region stimulates *transitions* between the states and disturbs the population levels; both this *excitation,* with a net absorption of energy, and the subsequent *relaxation* back to equilibrium may be analysed to give us information about the molecules of which the nuclei form a part. This book is devoted to these ideas and their applications in life sciences and medicine.

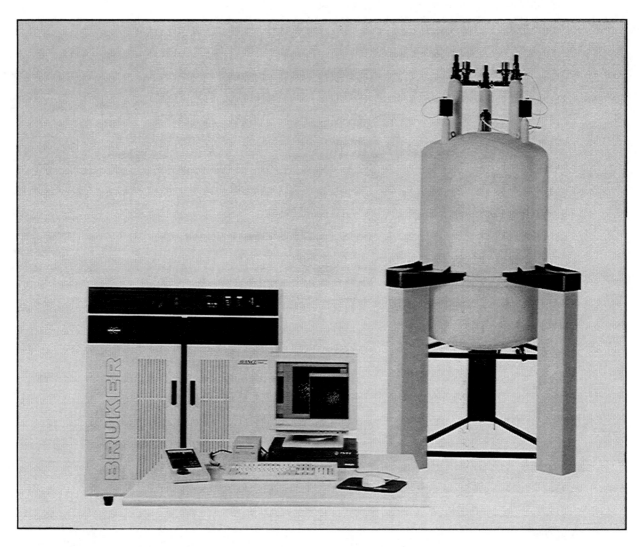

State-of-the-art: a 600-MHz high-resolution NMR spectrometer which uses digital technology for most stages of signal generation and detection. The cabinet at left contains major electronic control and data storage components: centre is the UNIX workstation through which the system is operated, and at right is the superconducting magnet. (See Section 3.3.) (Photograph courtesy of Bruker Spectrospin Ltd.)

CHAPTER 2: NMR IN ONE DIMENSION

How the properties of spin -$\frac{1}{2}$ nuclei lead to the basic NMR experiment

2.1 Properties of an isolated atomic nucleus.

Following the discussion of Chapter 1, we may put some numbers to the properties of any given atomic nucleus as follows:

The nucleus has a spin quantum number I which may be zero or some multiple of $\frac{1}{2}$. It has a corresponding *angular momentum* whose magnitude is:

$$\sqrt{I(I+1)}\hbar \quad \text{where } \hbar = \frac{h}{2\pi}$$

A nucleus for which I is not zero also has a *magnetic moment*. The size of the magnetic moment depends on I, and is given by γI where γ is a constant called the *magnetogyric ratio*. The value of γ differs from one type of nucleus to another (see the box on page 14). We will be particularly interested in nuclei for which I=$\frac{1}{2}$ (often called spin-$\frac{1}{2}$ nuclei): it happens that nuclei with odd mass numbers fulfil this condition. The nuclei of greatest value in biochemical NMR are ^{1}H, ^{13}C, ^{15}N, ^{19}F and ^{31}P, all of which are spin - $\frac{1}{2}$; some use is also made of deuterium, whose nucleus has I=1.

2.2 Isolated nucleus in a magnetic field

When a nucleus possessing a magnetic moment is placed in a magnetic field, we find:

(a) The nucleus exhibits *space quantisation* – at any given moment it can only be in one of (2I+1) permitted orientations relative to a direction in space (conventionally denoted the z direction). For I=$\frac{1}{2}$, of course, (2I+1)=2 and the nucleus must be in one of *two* directions in space relative to the z-direction.

(b) Each allowed orientation will have a slightly different energy. We can quantify this difference as follows: if the magnetic moment m of the nucleus has a component m_z in the z-direction, then the gap between the two energy levels for a spin-$\frac{1}{2}$ nucleus in an applied magnetic field B_0 (again along the z-direction) is $2m_zB_0$. Quantum mechanics tells us that if we can provide a quantum of electromagnetic energy equal to this energy gap, we can cause a transition between the levels. For a spin-$\frac{1}{2}$ nucleus with magnetogyric ratio γ, $m_z=h\gamma/4\pi$ so the energy of the quantum should be $E = h\nu = 2m_zB_0 = h\gamma B_0/2\pi$. Thus (cancelling the h) the frequency associated with the quantum of energy must be:

$$\nu = \gamma B_0/2\pi \quad \text{hertz}$$

(c) As we saw in Chapter 1, classically we may also regard the nucleus as having a precessional motion. This takes place at the Larmor frequency ν_0. which is directly proportional to the strength B_0 of the applied magnetic field:

$$\nu_0 = -\gamma B_0/2\pi \quad \text{hertz}$$

The observant reader will note that (apart from the sign) this frequency is exactly the same as that in the preceding paragraph: in other words, we can induce the nucleus to undergo a transition between its two energy states by irradiating it with electromagnetic radiation whose frequency is the same as its Larmor frequency. Because it is straightforward to determine the frequency of a radio signal, we can measure the Larmor frequency, and this measurement is right at the heart of NMR spectroscopy. A classical-formalism picture of how such transitions may be envisaged is presented in the next section.

2.3 Application of a second, varying field to a single nucleus

To picture how the application of electromagnetic radiation whose frequency is equal to the Larmor frequency of our nucleus can cause a transition between its energy states, imagine a situation in which we, as observers, are rotating *with* the nucleus at the Larmor frequency. Technically, we would be described as being in a *rotating frame of reference* – an idea which is of great value and to which we shall often return. The axes of the rotating frame of reference are designated x´, y´, z´: in this frame our precessing nuclear spin will appear stationary. We now apply a *new* magnetic field B_1, which is perpendicular to B_0 and is rotating – with us – about the z direction at the Larmor frequency. This field is of course stationary in the rotating frame. But as we saw in Chapter 1, *nuclei precess around*

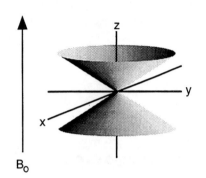

Precessing spin viewed in the laboratory (stationary) frame of reference.

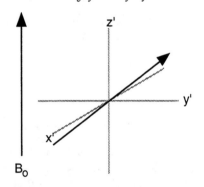

Precessing spin, viewed in the rotating frame of reference, appears stationary.

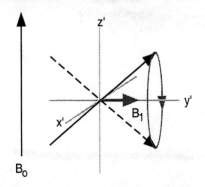

Application of a rotating magnetic field B_1 (stationary in the rotating frame) induces transitions between the two allowed states.

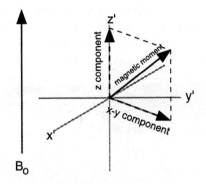

Components of a nuclear magnetic moment along the z direction and in the x-y plane.

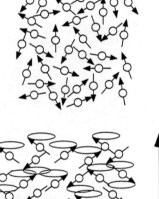

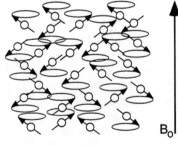

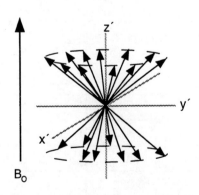

Population of spins: top, disordered in the absence of magnetic field; middle, aligned and precessing in applied field; bottom, brought to a common origin.

stationary magnetic fields, and so our spin will precess around B_1. In doing so it will pass between upper and lower energy states, thereby undergoing a transition between its two allowed orientations.

The next question is: how do you produce a field like B_1 that rotates about the z direction? It turns out to be easier than it sounds. Any electromagnetic radiation at a given frequency can be resolved into *components* which rotate in opposite directions at that frequency. Thus the rotating field B_1 can be produced simply by applying electromagnetic radiation at the Larmor frequency: B_1 is one of the components of this radiation. Of course, one quantum of this electromagnetic radiation has energy $h\gamma B_0/2\pi$ as required, since its frequency is the Larmor frequency.

Note, in passing, the mixed nature of this picture: we are using a classical image (precessing nuclei, rotating magnetic fields) to describe a quantum change (the jump of a nucleus between two energy levels). As pointed out in Chapter 1, such mixed metaphors must be used with care. Nevertheless, the picture is so useful that it is worth the risk!

2.4 Collective behaviour of a large number of nuclei: resultant magnetisation

As each individual nucleus precesses about B_0, its magnetic moment can be resolved into two components (diagram above, left): a z-component which is constant, and a component in the xy plane which rotates at the Larmor frequency. The effect of this single component on the world at large is truly infinitesimal; however, in a real NMR experiment we are never dealing with a single nucleus, but with a very large number of nuclei in the atoms and molecules of a solid or liquid sample. It is the *collective* behaviour of these nuclei that produces observable effects.

When we look at a large population of identical nuclei, we will find the following at equilibrium:

(a) The energy gap between upper and lower levels of a spin-$1/2$ nucleus is very small relative to thermal energies at normal temperatures, as expressed by kT. Consequently, the Boltzmann distribution tells us that the populations of the two states are very nearly equal. The z-components of the individual magnetic moments of the nuclei in the two states almost cancel out, but the small excess of spins in the lower energy level (aligned along B_0) means that there is a net magnetisation in this direction. The number of excess spins is given approximately by $h\nu/kT$, and their resultant magnetisation in the z direction is called M_z.

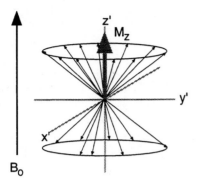

Resultant M_z of a number of spins at equilibrium.

B_0

(b) Although each individual nucleus contributes a rotating magnetic moment component in the xy plane, these are randomly arranged. Consequently, averaged over a large number of nuclei, there is no net magnetisation in this plane.

So the equilibrium state of a large number of nuclei in an applied field B_0 exhibits a small resultant magnetisation M_z in the same direction as B_0, and no other net magnetisation.

Box 2.1: Relative sensitivities

In theory, any nucleus with a non-zero spin quantum number can be used for NMR experiments. For biological applications, of course, we are restricted to those elements which occur naturally in biological systems or which can be introduced without altering the nature of the system. However, there are two other considerations: different nuclei respond with different sensitivities to the NMR experiment, and the isotopes which have nuclear spin $1/2$ are not always those which are most abundant in nature.

The sensitivity of a nucleus to NMR detection depends on three factors: the magnetogyric ratio (cubed), the spin quantum number I (squared), and the applied magnetic field (to the power $3/2$). Natural abundance varies greatly: 99.985% of all naturally occurring hydrogen atoms are the NMR-active ^1H isotope, 100% of natural phosphorus is ^{31}P, but only 1.1% of naturally-occurring carbon atoms are ^{13}C.

The two factors of sensitivity to NMR detection and relative abundance are often combined to give a figure for the *receptivity* of a particular nucleus. Receptivity is the product of relative abundance and sensitivity (at a constant field); the data shown in the table below is for the isotopes used most often in biological NMR applications, with the receptivities of the different nuclei set out relative to ^{13}C.

From the table we may draw some simple conclusions. One is the fortunate circumstance that hydrogen, the most ubiquitous atom in biological molecules, is also the easiest to perform NMR experiments on. Another is that if we wish to do very much with, say, ^{13}C, we will either need quite large quantities of sample or will need to use labelling methods, introducing ^{13}C in place of the more abundant and NMR-inactive ^{12}C, either generally or at specifically selected sites in the molecules.

Element	Isotope	Spin Quantum No.	Relative Abundance	Magnetogyric Ratio $\times 10^7$	Receptivity (relative to ^{13}C)	Larmor Frequency in 2.35 T field (MHz)
Hydrogen	^1H	1/2	99.98%	26.75	5670	100.00
Deuterium	^2H	1	0.02%	4.10	0.0082	15.35
Carbon	^{13}C	1/2	1.11%	6.73	1.00	25.15
Nitrogen	^{15}N	1/2	0.37%	-2.71	0.022	10.14
Fluorine	^{19}F	1/2	100%	25.19	4370	94.09
Phosphorus	^{31}P	1/2	100%	10.84	377	40.48

2.5 Effects of a pulse of radio-frequency radiation

Having specified the equilibrium state of a population of nuclei, we now begin the NMR experiment proper. We do this by causing nuclei to undergo transitions between their allowed energy states. If we apply a short but intense *pulse* of radiofrequency radiation at the Larmor frequency, a large number of such transitions will take place. The transition probability is the same for transitions in either direction, so:

(a) Rather more transitions will be from low energy to high energy – because slightly more nuclei were in the lower energy state to start with. This will reduce the Boltzmann population difference between the states, and M_z will be reduced. If the radiofrequency were to be applied for just long enough for every nucleus to undergo one transition, the population difference – and hence M_z – could even be inverted.

(b) The transitions, caused by B_1, *bring the spins into phase with B_1* and hence with each other, so that they precess together. Such concerted precession is termed *phase coherence* – another idea which we shall often return to. The word coherence comes from Latin roots meaning "to cling together", and adequately describes the action of the spins as they precess in concert with each other. Don't forget, however, that their togetherness is only based on the common starting point provided by B_1 and their common Larmor frequency; they precess together, but they are not forced to do so once B_1 is switched off. The resultant magnetisation in the xy plane is now no longer zero, but has a value M_{xy} – a net magnetisation rotating in the xy plane at the Larmor frequency. Detection of this rotating magnetisation, and hence of phase coherence, is the purpose of an NMR spectrometer; the creation, decay, and exchange of phase coherence ultimately provide us with the molecular information we seek. Note that it is possible, by controlling the phase of B_1, also to control the phase of M_{xy} – in other words, to determine whether it is initially in the x', $-x'$, y' or $-y'$ direction in the rotating frame, or somewhere in between. Applying B_1 along the $+x'$ axis will result in an M_{xy} initially in the $+y'$ direction in the rotating frame.

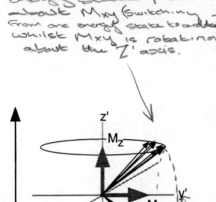

Magnetisation M_{xy} produced by phase coherence between spins after applied radiofrequency pulse.

2.6 The resultant magnetisation M

Thus the application of a radiofrequency pulse has reduced or inverted M_z, and introduced M_{xy}. The sum (or resultant) of these two magnetisations is called M. It is convenient to think of M as the result of *tilting* M_z away from the z axis. The longer or stronger the pulse applied, the greater will be the angle of tilt – so we may speak of a 30° pulse, or a 60° pulse, or even a 90° or 180° pulse. A 90° pulse is associated with a zero M_z and non-zero M_{xy}; a 180° pulse

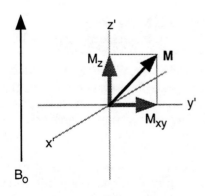

Resultant M of M_z and M_{xy}.

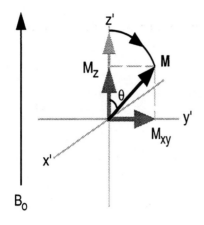

Flip angle θ.

inverts M_z from its original direction, and has zero M_{xy}. The usual term for the angle through which M_z is tilted by a pulse is the *flip angle*. So to define a pulse properly, it is necessary to specify its flip angle and the direction from which it is applied in the rotating frame, (e.g. 90°,+x).

Once we have the idea of the resultant magnetisation M, and of its components M_z and M_{xy}, it is often possible to describe what is happening in an NMR experiment by considering the changes that take place in M, rather than what is happening to individual spins. The original mathematical description of magnetic resonance given by Bloch is such a macroscopic treatment. Sometimes, however, it will be necessary to consider what might be happening to individual spins where this helps in understanding the behaviour of their resultant.

When the pulse of radiofrequency B_1 ends, the spin system returns over a period of time to its original state; this is the process called *relaxation*.

2.7 Relaxation

After a spin system has been perturbed in any way, it relaxes over a period of time (anything from milliseconds to minutes or more, depending on the system) to its equilibrium state. According to Bloch (and experimentally) this relaxation occurs exponentially, and we may best consider the relaxation of M_z and M_{xy} separately. Thus:

(a) M_z returns exponentially to its original value. This is called *longitudinal relaxation* (because it is *along* the direction of the applied magnetic field B_o), and occurs with a characteristic time T_1, the *longitudinal relaxation time*.

(b) M_{xy} decays exponentially to zero. This is *transverse relaxation*, and has a characteristic time T_2, the transverse relaxation time.

Of course, the relaxation of M_{xy} and M_z, which are the resultants of large numbers of individual nuclear magnetic moments, only happens because many individual nuclei separately undergo transitions between their allowed states. Taken together, these transitions will restore the original Boltzmann populations (thus restoring M_z to its equilibrium value) and will disrupt the phase coherence of the precession of the nuclear spins, thereby reducing M_{xy} to zero.

Because the energy gap between the two states is so small, the probability of transitions between energy states occurring spontaneously is negligible; thus the transitions which give rise to relaxation must be *caused* in some way. As we have already seen,

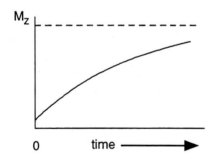

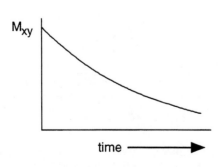

(Top) Mz returns exponentially to its equilibrium value.
(Bottom) Mxy decays exponentially to zero.

transitions are caused by irradiating the nuclei with radiation at their Larmor frequency, so since relaxation occurs without interference from outside the sample we must look *within* the sample for suitable sources of radiation.

In any real sample, there are two main sources of fluctuating magnetic fields which may have components at the Larmor frequency:

Firstly, we have general *magnetic noise*. Every molecule in the sample is moving (translating and rotating) relative to every other molecule: every molecule has many modes of vibrational motion: every molecule carries moving charges in the form of orbiting electrons and precessing nuclei. Thus every molecule is a source of rapidly fluctuating magnetic fields. In consequence every nucleus experiences continual and rapid (though small) variations in its local magnetic field as it tumbles in solution. It is in a *magnetically noisy* environment. The magnetic noise will contain many frequencies, but if some component of it is at the Larmor frequency of a given nucleus, and if this component is strong enough, it will cause transitions.

The spectrum of magnetic noise will vary according to the rate at which the molecules of the solution move, which is a function of molecular size and shape, temperature, and solution viscosity. Quantitatively, the rate of molecular motion may be described by translational and rotational *correlation times* which correspond roughly to the time taken for the molecule to translate through one molecular diameter or rotate through one radian. The most important determinants of the magnetic noise frequencies at a particular nucleus are the correlation times of the individual molecule of which it is a part. As a rule of thumb, for reasonably rigid molecules, correlation time increases linearly with molecular weight.

So if the spectrum of general magnetic noise has a component at the Larmor frequency of a group of nuclei, it can cause transitions, and these will tend both to dephase the spins (reducing M_{xy}) and to restore equilibrium Boltzmann populations (increasing M_z). In other words, this random magnetic noise causes both longitudinal and transverse relaxation. If the diagram (left, above) represents the power spectrum of the magnetic noise for three different situations, and if the required Larmor frequency corresponds to the arrow, we can see that this relaxation mechanism is most efficient for "intermediate" molecular motion, and less so for particularly fast- and slow-moving molecules. Thus molecules with intermediate correlation times give the most efficient longitudinal relaxation, and the shortest relaxation time T_1. They are also more efficient than fast-moving molecules at causing transverse relaxation, so the lower diagram at left shows that both T_1 and T_2 are related in the same way to correlation time in the fast-to-intermediate region of molecular motion. For reasons that will become clear, this part of the graph of relaxation times versus correlation time is called the *extreme narrowing region*.

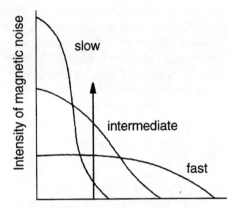

Spectra of magnetic noise for fast, intermediate and slow moving molecules. If the arrow represents the Larmor frequency of a nucleus, relaxation induced by magnetic noise will occur more quickly in a sample of intermediate rather than slow- or fast-moving molecules.

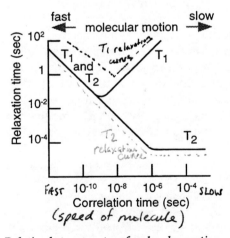

Relation between rates of molecular motion, as expressed by correlation times, and relaxation times for protons: the precise figures vary with spectrometer frequency.

The magnetic noise just described essentially accounts for all the variation of T_1 with molecular motion. With slow-moving molecules, however, there is an additional contribution to T_2: spin exchange. If molecules spend long times near each other, it becomes possible for nuclei having the same Larmor frequency to *mutually exchange energy* while undergoing simultaneous transitions. Effectively two precessing spins, one in a high energy state and the other in a low energy state, can irradiate each other at their Larmor frequency, so that each undergoes a transition. This is *spin exchange*; it occurs randomly, so if the spins involved were precessing in phase with other spins before the exchange, it is unlikely that they will be doing so afterwards. This is a loss of phase coherence; there are now fewer spins precessing together, and M_{xy} is reduced. Spin exchange contributes to transverse relaxation, but of course the relative populations of the two energy states are unaltered by spin exchange and so there is no contribution to T_1. Spin exchanges occur more efficiently the longer the spins stay close to each other, so T_2 gets shorter when molecules are slow moving; T_2 values are very short indeed for solid samples. Thus T_2 continues to decrease with longer correlation times; the corresponding region of the graph is called the *spin-diffusion region*.

Relaxation times are very important both as probes of molecular motion and also because the Bloch treatment shows that the *widths of the lines* in an NMR spectrum are *proportional to $1/T_2$* – in other words, slow-moving molecules with short T_2 values give broad lines in the NMR spectrum.

2.8 Detection of NMR

The experiment we have performed so far is as follows: a sample containing atomic nuclei with spin quantum number $\frac{1}{2}$ is placed in a strong constant magnetic field, with the field defining the z direction in space. As a result of the field, a small net nuclear magnetisation M_z is induced, and each nucleus precesses, independently of the others, at its Larmor frequency. We then apply a short but intense pulse of radiofrequency radiation to the sample; this results in a reduction or inversion of M_z and the appearance of phase coherence which results in magnetisation M_{xy} rotating in the xy plane with the Larmor frequency of the chosen nuclei.

Consider one such M_{xy}. A small wire coil placed near the sample will detect the varying field from this rotating magnetisation; the current thus induced in the coil will vary sinusoidally, oscillating at the frequency of M_{xy}. Further, it will decay to zero as transverse relaxation occurs. Such a signal is called a *free induction decay* (FID for short), and looks like the diagram at left. If we represent this signal on a *spectrum* (a plot of intensity against frequency) we will find a single line representing the frequency of the oscillations, with the linewidth of the line dependent on the rate of decay of the FID;

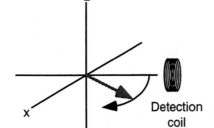

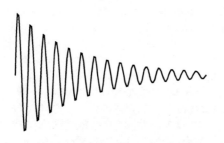

*Rotating M_{xy} is picked up by the detector coil to produce the **free induction decay** signal (below).*

fast decay leads to broad lines. So the frequency of the waves in the FID will determine the frequency of the line in the spectrum, and the rate of decay of the FID (determined by T_2) controls its linewidth.

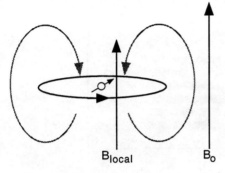

Diamagnetic effect means that the local magnetic field at the nucleus is less than the applied field B_0.

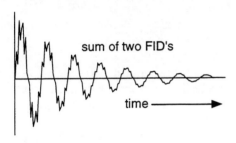

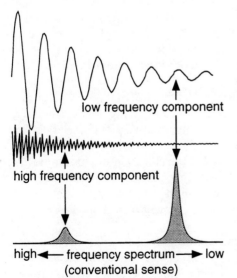

An FID made up of two frequencies (top), its components (centre) and its frequency spectrum (bottom).

2.9 The chemical shift

The Larmor frequency of a given nucleus is proportional to the total magnetic field B_{local} at the nucleus. In the discussion so far we have assumed this to be equal to the applied field B_0, but if the nucleus is surrounded by an electron cloud (as it will be if it is part of a molecule) the motion of the electrons, induced by the application of B_0 itself, will alter the local field at the nucleus (moving charges produce magnetic fields – see Chapter 1). This *diamagnetic* effect produces a small but significant opposing field within the electron cloud, so that the field B_{local} at the nucleus is slightly smaller than the externally applied field B_0. The nucleus is said to be *shielded* by the electrons. The exact magnitude of this shielding effect depends on the distribution and density of the electron cloud, which in turn depends on the nature of the molecule of which it forms a part. Thus nuclei of the same element which are in differing *chemical environments* within a molecule will have different Larmor frequencies. This effect is called the *chemical shift* and enables us to distinguish one chemical environment from another in the same molecule. The variation is small; most ^1H frequencies vary only within a range of ten parts per million, and although ^{13}C frequencies can vary over a range of hundreds of parts per million, this is still less than 1% variation of their Larmor frequency. Fortunately, frequency is one of the quantities which can be most readily measured with modern electronics; although the chemical shift effects are so small, they can be measured with very great accuracy.

Given that nuclei in different chemical environments will have different Larmor frequencies, we may conclude that if we can make the applied pulse of radiofrequency radiation excite, say, all the hydrogen nuclei in a given sample, the FID which results will be a mixture of many different frequencies. If we can sort these out and plot them on a spectrum, the spectrum will display a separate peak for each chemical environment in which hydrogen atoms find themselves in the sample. Because the diamagnetic and other effects which cause chemical shift are proportional to the applied field (and hence to the Larmor frequency) the chemical shift axis of the spectrum can be calibrated in parts per million of the Larmor frequency. Conventionally this is done with Larmor frequency increasing from right to left on the spectrum.

Many effects contribute to the precise chemical shift of a given nucleus, and it is only possible to predict in rather general terms where a given nucleus will fall on the spectrum. It is thus not possible to assign a resonance to a particular chemical environment

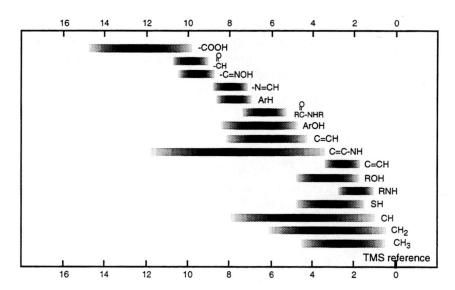

Regions of the proton spectrum, showing proton chemical shifts arising from different chemical environments. Chemical shifts are shown in parts per million from TMS, a reference compound (see 2.11(a)).

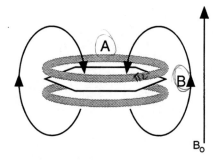

Strong diamagnetic effect of an aromatic ring; a nucleus at A will be strongly shielded, a nucleus at B will be strongly deshielded.

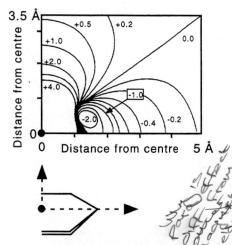

Contours showing chemical shift effect at positions relative to a benzene ring.

in the molecule simply on the basis of its chemical shift. There are generalisations to be made, however: a spectrum will have a "methyl region", or an "aromatic region", for example. An indication of these regions for proton spectra are given above.

More details of some mechanisms of chemical shift are given in Box 2.2. However there are two additional sources of chemical shift which are of particular importance in biological applications:

The first of these is the *ring-current shift*. The π-system of an aromatic ring (tyrosine, phenylalanine, histidine in one of its ionisation states, nucleic acid bases) is made up of a number of electrons and in an applied magnetic field exhibits a powerful diamagnetic effect. The result is to *shield* nuclei at position A in the diagram (i.e. reduce their local magnetic field and hence their Larmor frequency) and to *de-shield* nuclei at position B. The effect is very sensitive to the relative positions and distances of the different groups, and may shift peaks on the NMR spectrum by several parts per million from their intrinsic chemical shift. A quantitative plot of the effect for a benzene ring is shown at left, in a *Johnson-Bovey* diagram. The hydrophobic cores of proteins often contain aromatic amino acids tightly packed with other hydrophobic residues such as leucine or valine; analysis of ring-current shifts has yielded valuable information concerning the precise arrangement of such groups.

A second extrinsic shift mechanism arises from the presence of a *paramagnetic ion* (e.g. Fe, Mn, Gd) inside a protein molecule. Such an ion is a source of local magnetic fields, and may perturb the Larmor frequencies of nuclei nearby; there may also be relaxation effects which will be mentioned later. The effect of a bound paramagnetic ion is rigorously distance- and direction- dependent and provides a powerful probe of the region surrounding the ion. Paramagnetic ions may, of course, be introduced artificially into the structure of a protein, for example by replacing the naturally occurring magnesium ion of lysozyme by manganese or one of the lanthanide series of elements. This method provided some of the classic early studies of macromolecular structure by NMR, but has fallen from favour as the development of two-dimensional NMR methods, described in Chapter 4, has provided new and even more powerful analytical tools.

Box 2.2: More About Chemical Shift

In the absence of effects due to ring-currents or local paramagnetic ions, the field at a given nucleus depends on the electron cloud which exists in its immediate neighbourhood. In general, this cloud will be asymmetric, and so the shielding will be different in different directions in space. This *anisotropy* is of prime importance in solid-state NMR; however, in liquid-state high resolution studies the variations average out as the molecule tumbles in solution. The averaged effect is expressed in terms of a shielding factor σ, so that the effective local field B_{local} at the nucleus is given by $B_{local} = B_0(1-\sigma)$. Because σ represents a very small fraction of the applied field, it is expressed in *parts per million*. The observed chemical shift (that is, the value of σ) for a given nucleus is a function of several factors:

1. The atomic shielding (*diamagnetic effect*) mentioned in the main text. This is produced by circulation of the electrons associated with the particular atom containing the nucleus under observation.

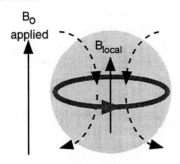

B_{local} within electron cloud is reduced by induced motion of electrons. (Effect on B_{local} is exaggerated.)

Electron density depends of course on the atomic number of the atom, but will also depend on the electron-donating or electron-withdrawing nature of neighbouring atoms in the same molecule. For example, a hydrogen atom attached by a covalent bond to an oxygen atom will have a reduced electron density due to the electronegative nature of oxygen. The proton of an O-H hydrogen atom will thus be less shielded than that of a C-H hydrogen atom: B_{local} will be slightly greater, and so the Larmor frequency will be proportionately larger.

2. A *neighbour paramagnetic effect* which is produced by the electrons of neighbouring atoms in the molecule. This may shield or deshield the nucleus depending on (a) the orientation of the molecule relative to the applied field and (b) the way in which the energy states of these electrons are modified by the field. The effect observed is the average of these effects over all orientations. Some electronic structures, such as double or triple (acetylenic) C-C bonds are particularly strongly influenced by the applied field and produce relatively large paramagnetic contributions to the chemical shift.

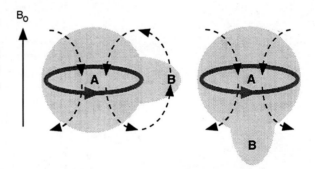

B_{local} at B depends on the orientation of molecule AB.

3. Other effects, including:

Hydrogen bonding. The Larmor frequency for a proton involved in a hydrogen bond will be raised slightly. The mechanism by which this occurs is complex, but the effect can be valuable in estimating the strength of the bond.

Solvent. Polar groups will interact with polar solvents, usually with the effect of strengthening electronegative effects such as those mentioned in 1 above. Nonpolar solvents may have an effect if their molecules react very anisotropically to a magnetic field. In addition, of course, a solvent may interact directly with molecules of solute, for example by forming hydrogen bonds with them. Such effects are occasionally put to use by, for example, using a solvent which contains paramagnetic ions which have a particularly strong effect on the chemical shift or relaxation properties of exposed groups on the surface of a solute molecule.

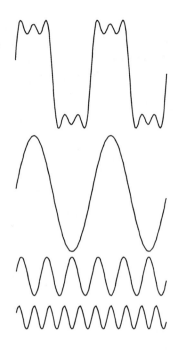

*A complex repeating waveform (top) and
its harmonic components.*

2.10 Sorting out the FID: the Fourier transform

The FID which is detected after a sample has been excited by a
pulse of radiofrequency will normally be a mixture of many
different frequencies, and presents a very complicated waveform.
The problem is compounded by the fact that each group of chemically identical nuclei may have a different transverse relaxation
time T_2 from the others, so that the different frequencies that make
up the FID will all decay at different rates. The problem is to
analyse this waveform into the individual Larmor frequencies that
make it up, so that an NMR spectrum may be plotted: the solution
is found in the powerful mathematical methods devised nearly two
centuries ago by Jean Baptiste Joseph Fourier during his studies on
heat flow.

Fourier theory tells us that any waveform which repeats itself
indefinitely with time can be analysed into a series of discrete sine
or cosine waves (its *harmonic components*). There may be very many
of these, but they are all separate. The mathematical expression
which gives the harmonic components of a given repeating waveform is called a *Fourier series*.

When the waveform does not repeat itself indefinitely, it cannot be
constructed from a *finite* number of discrete components. It can,
however, be considered to be equivalent to the sum of an *infinite*
number of frequencies, forming a *continuum*. In this case it is not
possible to describe separate frequency components, but it is still
possible by means of a mathematical integration known as *Fourier
transformation* to construct the *spectrum* of the components, a plot
showing the intensity of each component on a continuous frequency scale. Some examples of mathematical functions and their
Fourier transforms are given in Box 2.3. The simplest example, and
the most useful for NMR, is the Fourier transform of a single
harmonic (sine or cosine) wave. If the wave is indefinitely long, its
transform is a single very sharp line on a frequency scale (a so-
called delta function). If the wave is cut short in some way, the
resultant spectrum given by Fourier transformation is still centred
on a single frequency, but has a finite linewidth.

Such a spectrum reveals that a cut-short (truncated) sinewave (such
as, for example, a short pulse of radiofrequency radiation) is made
up of a *continuous band* of frequencies which are centred on the
original frequency of the sinewave. This is good news when we
want to excite all the Larmor frequencies in a given sample: if our
pulse of radiofrequency is short, the sample will see it as made up
of a continuous band of frequencies wide enough to cover all the
frequencies we need. The precise shape of this band of frequencies
depends on the way in which the wave is cut short (whether, for
example, it is cut off sharply or simply decays gently to zero).
Further, the width of the band depends on the overall duration of

Box 2.3: Fourier Transform Pairs

Fourier transformation is a mathematical process (here represented by FT) which interconverts two functions. Below are Fourier pairs which are important in NMR.

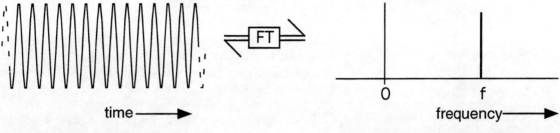

Infinite sinewave, frequency f   *"Delta function" at frequency f*

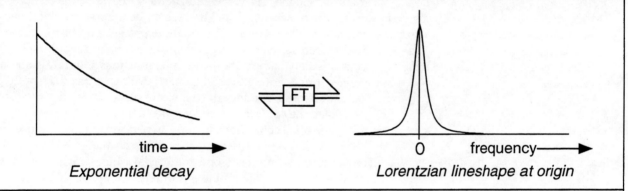

Exponential decay   *Lorentzian lineshape at origin*

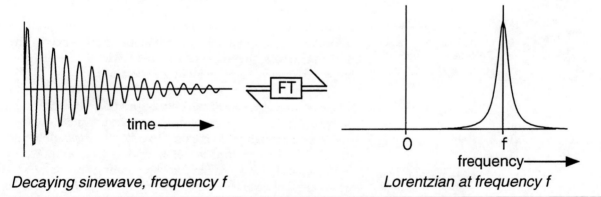

Decaying sinewave, frequency f   *Lorentzian at frequency f*

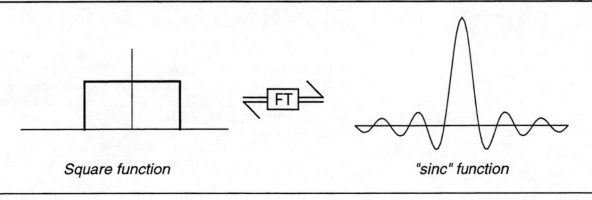

Square function   *"sinc" function*

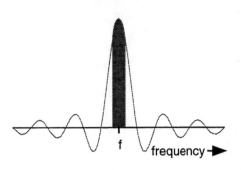

A square pulse of radiofrequency (top) and the useful part of its frequency spectrum (shaded): in practice, the rest of the spectrum is filtered out electronically.

the waveform – the longer it lasts, the narrower the band. (For an infinitely long wave, the band becomes infinitely narrow, and we again have the delta function)

Thus when we set up the pulse of radiofrequency which starts off the NMR experiment, we need to control both its length and its intensity. It must be short enough to contain all the Larmor frequencies of the sample, and powerful enough to cause the desired flip angle in the net magnetisation. In addition its phase must be controlled so that, in the rotating frame, it is directed along the desired axis. It may also be useful to control the shape of the pulse: more details will be found in Chapter 3.

Now we come to the FID itself. It is a combination of a number of different Larmor frequencies, all decaying at different rates, and singularly uninformative to look at. If we could perform a Fourier transform on the FID, we would get the spectrum of the components which make it up, and that would be the spectrum of chemical shifts that we require. This ought to present a problem, because Fourier transformation is a process which can strictly only be performed on mathematically defined functions. Our FID is not so defined, but is simply the result of an NMR experiment. Happily, it is still possible to produce the transform using an iterative calculation called the *fast Fourier transform algorithm* which runs on even relatively small computers. In order to perform a transform using this method, the waveform must be *digitised* – that is, its value must be sampled at a number (some hundreds or thousands) of points to provide the input data for the computer. Two things should be noted with regard to this digitisation:

(a) Accurate digitisation of a harmonic (sine or cosine) waveform can only be achieved if it is sampled at least *twice per cycle*. This implies that sampling must take place at twice the frequency of the highest frequency component in the spectrum.

(b) An accurate transform can only be produced if sufficient data points are available to start with. In practice this means sampling over a long enough period of time to collect a large number of data points – the rule of thumb is that to produce a spectrum with a resolution of R hertz (i.e. effectively separating lines in the spectrum which are R hertz apart) it is necessary to sample for a period of at least 1/R seconds. Thus if we need our spectrum to display lines 0.5 Hz apart, we should collect data for at least two seconds.

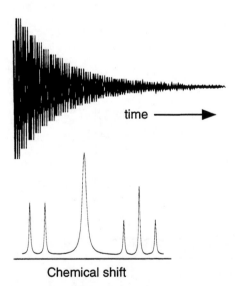

A "real" FID and part of its spectrum.

To summarise: the FID from a real sample is a mixture of waves, all at different frequencies and all decaying at different rates – but the process of Fourier transformation sorts out this information and presents us with the spectrum of all the various Larmor frequencies, each with its own T_2 and hence its own linewidth, of the nuclei in the sample molecules.

In the strong magnetic fields used for NMR, the FID is made up of very high frequencies of many megahertz; these are difficult to digitise simply because they are so high. However, the frequencies are spread over a very small range, and this provides a way of handling the problem. After all, we are not really interested in the Larmor frequency as such, but only in the amount by which it varies from one molecular environment to another – the chemical shift. This variation is tiny relative to the Larmor frequency itself, so we can reduce our data handling problem by subtracting a fixed frequency, very close to the Larmor frequency, from the FID before we digitise it. Then instead of having to sample and digitise a signal of many MHz frequency, we are working with only a few kHz. These low frequencies, in the audiofrequency range, are very readily handled by modern electronics. The process of measuring very small differences between very large numbers is rather analogous to determining the thickness of the paint on top of the Eiffel Tower by first measuring the overall height and then subtracting the height of the ironwork; fortunately we can generate and measure frequencies with very great accuracy.

To take an example, consider an NMR experiment on protons in a magnetic field of 6.4 tesla. At this field the basic Larmor frequency is 270 MHz. Proton chemical shifts vary by up to about 10 parts per million, so the spectrum covers a range of about 2700 Hz. We irradiate the sample with a short pulse of radiofrequency at 270 MHz, making sure that the frequency we use is higher (or lower) than any of the Larmor frequencies in the sample: the reason for this will become clear in section 3.4. Because the pulse is short it contains a continuum of frequencies a few kilohertz either side of the main frequency, so all the protons in the sample will be excited. The resulting FID is detected and amplified, and then the fundamental 270 MHz frequency is subtracted from it. We are left with an FID which contains frequencies from some low value, say x, to x+2700 Hz. We must sample this at least twice per cycle, so we collect a minimum of 5400 data points per second. If the resulting spectrum after transformation is to show detail as fine as 2 Hz, this data must be collected for at least 0.5 seconds – a total of 2700 data points to store and process. This would be quite typical for one-dimensional NMR, though in the binary world of the computer it would be more usual to collect 2048 or 4096 data points.

A helpful image at this point is to consider the rotating frame of reference. If our frame of reference is rotating at exactly 270 MHz, and one of the spins in the sample is rotating 1 kHz faster than this, the spin will be rotating at 1 kHz *in the rotating frame*. This is the frequency that will be revealed by the process of subtraction described above, so in the rotating frame we may simply think of the spin as precessing at 1 kHz. In other words, the subtraction process effectively puts us into the rotating frame; we can forget about the fundamental Larmor frequency and concentrate simply on the chemical shifts – the differences between the chemical-shifted Larmor frequencies of the sample and the fundamental reference frequency of the rotating frame. We shall make more use of this image later.

2.11 The high-resolution NMR spectrum.

Having collected and transformed our FID, we have a standard one-dimensional NMR spectrum. This is shown schematically in Figure 2.3, and is characterised by five parameters:

(a) The **chemical shift**, or position of the resonances on the frequency scale, usually expressed in parts per million of the Larmor frequency. Because this is a relative measurement, we conventionally measure it by comparison to the signal from a *reference compound* in the sample. Such a standard compound should have a chemical shift which is stable under different solution conditions: for proton spectra in non-aqueous solvents, the standard is *tetramethyl silane* (TMS) and the chemical-shift axis will be labelled something like 'ppm from TMS'. As stated earlier, and for historical reasons, the spectrum is laid out with the lowest Larmor frequencies (most highly shielded nuclei) to the right; again for historical reasons this is known as the 'high field' region of the spectrum. A resonance signal which moves to the right on such a display is described as having undergone an 'upfield shift'.

(b) The **area** under each resonance signal. This is simply proportional to the number of nuclei in the sample which contribute to that resonance, so that the area of a CH_3 proton resonance will be three times that of a CH resonance from the same molecule.

(c) The **width** of the resonances, measured in hertz at half the peak height. The width of a line is a function of T_2 (see section 2.7) and hence of molecular motion within the sample.

In addition to the three parameters chemical shift, area, and width, there are two which we have not yet considered: *multiplicity* and *coupling constant*. These have a common origin: the interaction between nuclear spins which are close to each other in the same molecule. So we add to our list:

(d). The **multiplicity** of each resonance – whether it is a singlet, doublet, quartet etc. (see section 2.12).

(e). The **separation** of the components of each multiplet. This is known as the *coupling constant* and given the symbol J Hz.

Note that while chemical shift is proportional to the applied field, and is expressed in parts per million of the spectrometer frequency, both linewidths and coupling constants are essentially independent of field and are measured directly in hertz.

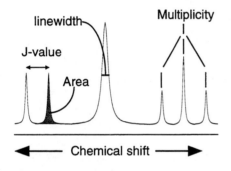

The five parameters of a high-resolution NMR spectrum.

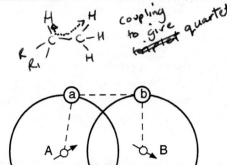

coupling
to give quartet
triplet ~~quartet~~

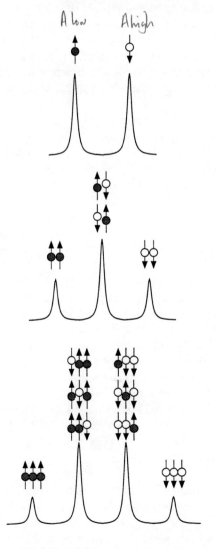

Coupling between nucleus A and nucleus B via their electrons a and b.

A low   A high

Doublet, triplet and quartet patterns.

2.12 Multiplicity of NMR resonances

Are A and B both protons or is 1 H and 1 N's

The energy of the orbital motion of electrons is affected by the magnetic moment of the nucleus of the atom, and of course in a molecule the electrons of the constituent atoms interact with each other. Thus the orientation of nuclear spin A, acting via the electrons of the bonds between them, will affect the local magnetic environment of nucleus B. Since A has two possible orientations the nucleus B will have two possible and slightly different energies; in a sample consisting of a large number of molecules half the molecules will be in each state. Thus in a resonance experiment two Larmor frequencies will be seen for B and it will appear as a *doublet*. The effect is known as *spin-spin splitting, scalar coupling,* or *J-coupling;* the separation of the two components of the signal from B is expressed as J Hz.

A preliminary consideration of the effect would conclude that because the populations of the two possible states of A are virtually equal, the two components of the B doublet will appear equal in size. This is true provided the coupling is *weak;* weak coupling is defined as that for which J is small relative to the difference in chemical shift between A and B. If this condition is not met, the sizes of the components will vary; such *strong coupling* is described below. Since scalar coupling is mediated by the electrons a and b, the value of J will depend on the nature and orientation of the bonds between atom Aa and atom Bb. Coupling effects can be transmitted through as many as 7 bonds, but at that range they are small and three-bond couplings are most often of use in the analysis of macromolecular structure. Typical values of proton-proton splittings vary from J = 0.1 Hz to J = 10 Hz or so. Coupling constants between other nuclei can be much larger.

There are some important things to note about J:

(a) The splitting of B's signal by A is identical to the splitting of A's signal by B. Identical J values can be useful in determining which nuclei are coupled to each other in a molecule.

(b) If there is more than one "A" nucleus, B will have a resonance split into more than 2 components – see diagrams at left. With two identical "A" neighbours, B's signal will be a *triplet* with components of relative area 1:2:1. With three identical neighbours (a methyl group, say) it becomes a *quartet* with relative areas 1:3:3:1.

(c) The value of J depends on the nature of the bonds between A and B, and this includes the dihedral angle (defined on page 71). The dependence is described by the *Karplus relationship*. This is derived from many empirical observations, and is illustrated (next page) for a simple HC-CH case; the curve is described by an equation of the form:

$$J = P\,cos^2\phi + Q\,cos\phi + R$$

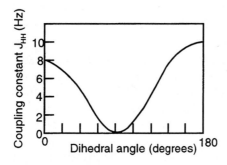

Form of the Karplus relationship for coupling between protons in an H-C-C-H group with dihedral angle φ.

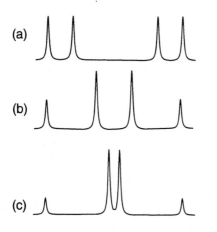

Weak coupling pattern (a) and strong coupling patterns (b and c).

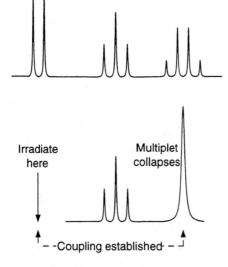

Determination of coupling between resonances by spin-decoupling (see text).

where P, Q, and R are constants. For the coupling between αCH and βCH protons of amino acids, P, Q, and R are 9.5, 1.6 and 1.8 respectively, while for coupling between αCH and peptide NH (the φ-angle) they are 6.4, 1.4 and 1.9. The shape of the curve implies some ambiguities in the interpretation of J values: a given J may correspond to more than one dihedral angle. Large J-values are less likely to be ambiguous than small ones.

(d) Simple splitting patterns are only observed in the weak coupling case, where J is many times smaller than the chemical-shift separation δ of nuclei A and B in the spectrum. As the signals from A and B come closer together in the spectrum δ approaches J and we move into the area of *strong coupling*; the intensities of the outer components are reduced. A convention in describing spin coupling in these cases is to use letters that are far apart in the alphabet (A,X) to describe resonances far apart in the spectrum, and closer ones (A,B) for cases of stronger coupling. Thus the weakly coupled quartet (a) at left would be an AX pattern while (c) would be described as an AB quartet. In the extreme strong-coupling case, the signals overlap and have the same chemical shift, the splitting disappears and we are left with a single line. A full description of the strong coupling case requires quantum-mechanical analysis.

Another term frequently used to describe the difference between the weak and strong coupling regimes is to describe weakly-coupled spectra as *first-order* and strongly coupled ones as *second order*. For first-order spectra, the chemical shift difference $\Delta\delta$ between two resonances must be large (in Hz) compared to their J value. But chemical shift in Hz is proportional to the applied field, while J values are not: thus raising the operating frequency of the spectrometer can simplify a second-order pattern into a first-order one: $\Delta\delta$ stays the same in ppm, but increases in Hz.

(e) Of course, the multiplet resonance of a given nucleus can be split again by other neighbouring groups, to give more complex patterns still. (If the chemical shifts are far apart, this may give an AMX pattern.) The normal approach to untangling this problem in one-dimensional NMR is the technique of *spin-decoupling* (diagram, left). In this, the observation of one peak is performed while a steady low-power radiofrequency is applied at the Larmor frequency of a nucleus suspected of being coupled to it. The rapid and continual transitions caused by this irradiation lead to an averaging of the spin coupling between the nuclei, which thus collapses the multiplet being observed: the collapse to a singlet provides evidence of the suspected coupling.

(f) J-coupling and multiplet patterns are perhaps the most important parameters in the structure determination of small molecules. Chemists have for many years used J-values transmitted through up to seven bonds, and the quantum mechanical analysis of these is a key factor in small-molecule structure analysis. In larger molecules J-couplings are, more often than not, totally obscured by the line broadening produced by short T_2 values;

however when they can be observed they remain of great value. Long range couplings are rarely observable for large molecules, even at 600 MHz and with resolution enhancement (section 3.5(e)), but three-bond couplings of anything up to 15-20 Hz can quite often be measured. In two-dimensional NMR the techniques of J-resolved and multiple-quantum-filtered COSY spectroscopy can enhance the resolution and measurement of J-values. Two-dimensional techniques will be covered in Chapter 4.

2.13 Chemical exchange and other spectrum-perturbing phenomena

2.13.1 Chemical exchange.

Molecular structures are in a state of dynamic, rather than static equilibrium. Simple instances may be found in the exchange of protons between solvent water and carboxyl or amino groups, rotation about bonds, the (Enzyme+Substrate ⇔ Enzyme/Substrate) equilibrium, or the 'rippling' of helical segments up and down a polypeptide chain. In such cases a nucleus will not be continuously in one magnetic environment, but rather exchanging at some rate between two or more environments. The effect that this has on the spectrum depends on (a) the chemical shift difference between the environments and (b) the rate of exchange between environments.

When the exchange rate is *very slow* (compared with the chemical shift difference between the two environments, expressed in Hz), the nucleus precesses many times in one environment before moving to the other. In this case a separate signal will be observed for each environment, the relative sizes of the signals being a measure of the relative numbers of nuclei in each environment at a given time and hence of the equilibrium constant for the exchange reaction. If the exchange is *very fast*, nuclei do not stay long enough in either environment to adjust their frequencies and so effectively precess at an average frequency. This gives a single peak whose *position* is a measure of the relative time spent in each environment; again, this yields the equilibrium constant. For *intermediate* exchange rates, the spectrum varies between these extremes. Model spectra for a simple case are shown in the diagram at left. In the intermediate range, equilibrium constants are not so easy to acquire; however it is possible to use the lineshapes to get a good idea of the exchange rate. In fast- or slow-exchange cases, only a lower or upper bound may be placed on exchange rates.

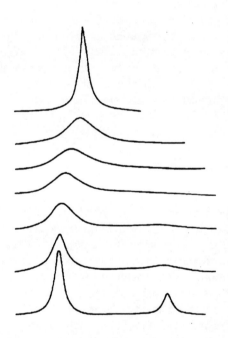

Effects of echange between two environments: fast exchange (top) to very slow exchange (bottom). Intermediate spectra show exchange rates similar to the difference between the chemical shifts of the resonances, expressed in Hz.

2.13.2 Local paramagnetic relaxation probes.

As described above under the chemical shift heading, paramagnetic ions (i.e. those with unpaired electron spins) can produce local magnetic perturbations within a molecule. Such ions may be divided into classes according to whether they have short electronic relaxation times, and cause extra chemical shifts without significant broadening (an example is Eu^{+++}), or longer relaxation times, causing broadening without significant shifts (e.g. Mn^{++}, Gd^{+++}, Eu^{++}, Cu^{++} and V^{++}). Relaxation may be caused by such ions either by direct dipole-dipole interactions or by *scalar* or *hyperfine* coupling transmitted through a chemical bond. The *Solomon-Bloembergen equations* which govern the effect of a paramagnetic ion on the relaxation times of nuclei bound nearby are complex; however, broadening effects (which depend on r^{-6}, where r is the distance between the paramagnetic centre and the nucleus under observation) can give useful information on distances relative to a paramagnetic ion bound, say, at the active site of an enzyme, while shift effects give information about direction as well as distance. The effects of paramagnetics on a protein can usefully be analysed using *difference spectroscopy* – the classic experiments employed differences between spectra taken with different lanthanide ions at the active sites of metalloenzymes. Elements of the lanthanide series are chemically identical but magnetically different, while lanthanum itself is diamagnetic, thus providing a useful control for difference spectra.

2.13.3 Nuclear quadrupole effects.

The distribution of electric charge in most nuclei is symmetrical; thus local *electric* fields have no effect on them. Nuclei which do have an asymmetrical distribution of electric charge (a *nuclear electric quadrupole moment*) are very sensitive to varying local electric fields. None of the nuclei normally considered for biological NMR have electric quadrupole moments themselves; effects may nevertheless be seen in the NMR spectra of nuclei whose *neighbouring* nuclei have quadrupole moments. The prime example of this in proton spectroscopy is ^{14}N. This has no magnetic moment and thus takes no part in NMR itself; however it does have an electric quadrupole moment and so the varying electric fields in a tumbling molecule cause it to change its spin state (it has 3 allowed orientations) very rapidly. This enhances the transverse relaxation of any proton attached to the nitrogen atom, and broadens its resonance.

Any H attatched to an N atom will relax transversally quicker. ie shorter T_2 time and ∴ broader peaks in spectrum.

CHAPTER 3: TOPICS IN 1D NMR

More ideas relevant to biochemical applications of NMR

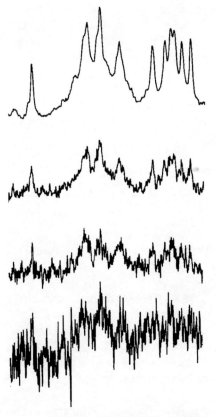

Signal-to-noise improvement by accumulating repeated FID's. Bottom to top: 1, 16, 100, 7500 repetitions.

3.1 Signal-to-noise

One of the consequences of using a low-sensitivity method like NMR is that the signals detected are weak, and need considerable amplification. All amplifiers are subject to internal noise due to random motions of the electrons in their circuits, and although this noise is very small, the currents induced by the precessing magnetisation in the sample may be hardly any greater. Consequently, the FID which is detected following a single pulse will frequently be buried in randomly-fluctuating noise and will transform into a very noisy spectrum. However, a major advantage of pulse-Fourier transform NMR is that the FID can be collected in a short time, often less than a second, and this gives the opportunity to enhance the signal-to-noise ratio by *signal averaging*. This is simply the collecting and averaging of a large number of identical FID's. Noise varies randomly in amplitude and phase from one FID to the next, and so tends to cancel out over a number of repeated experiments, while genuine signals, the same each time, accumulate. The improvement is proportional to the square root of the number of FID's collected: in other words, to improve the signal-to-noise ratio by a factor of ten, a hundred FID's will need to be averaged. At a second each, this still only takes a couple of minutes. As greater enhancements are required, we enter the area of diminishing returns. A hundredfold improvement would take 10,000 seconds in our example (about $2\frac{1}{2}$ hours). A thousandfold improvement would need a million seconds, or nearly a fortnight! Examples of signal-to-noise enhancement are shown at left.

Sample in a standard 5 mm NMR tube.

3.2 The sample

As we have already said, NMR is an inherently insensitive technique when compared to, say, UV spectrophotometry. We thus need to work with amounts and concentrations of sample which are very high compared to many other techniques, and this can be a serious limitation. Of course, it is possible to get a signal of sorts out of practically nothing, given enough time to accumulate thousands of FID's, but the resulting spectra will probably be pretty unconvincing and the queue of other spectrometer users will start to complain!

As an example, we consider the amount of sample needed for proton NMR; more will be needed for other nuclei (see Box 2.1, page 14). For comfort, aim to work with perhaps 0.5 ml of solution at a concentration around millimolar (1 mM) for one-dimensional NMR; for two-, three-, or four-dimensional spectroscopy, greater concentrations are desirable. One-millimolar translates into 10 milligrams per millilitre (mg/ml) for a macromolecule of 10,000 daltons, so the 0.5 ml sample would contain at least 5 mg of solute. Of course, this presupposes that the sample molecules are soluble at this concentration without aggregation in the chosen solvent. The sample must also be free from any particulate matter (it may need filtering through a glass-wool plug), and particularly from any paramagnetic impurities, which cause line broadening or chemical shift perturbations. Oxygen is paramagnetic, and dissolved oxygen may need to be purged from the sample for critical applications. Samples are normally placed in the spectrometer in glass tubes of 5 mm outside diameter; since for the highest resolution the sample may be spun at high speed to average out magnetic field inhomogeneities, tubes need to be made to high standards of precision in straightness and wall thickness.

Schematic cross-section of a superconducting high-resolution NMR magnet.

3.3 The spectrometer

A block diagram of an NMR spectrometer is shown opposite. The main components are as follows:

(a) A *frequency source*. This synthesises the main radiofrequencies for use throughout the spectrometer. We need to generate signals at the Larmor frequencies of each isotope (nucleus type) we intend to observe or decouple, as well as for the field-frequency lock (see (c) below). The main frequency used as a basis for a particular experiment is often called the *carrier* frequency.

(b) A *pulse gate and shaper*. The whole NMR enterprise relies on the accurate shaping, timing, and phase of the pulses which are applied to the sample. Complex 3D experiments may require trains of dozens of pulses at several different frequencies, each with a very

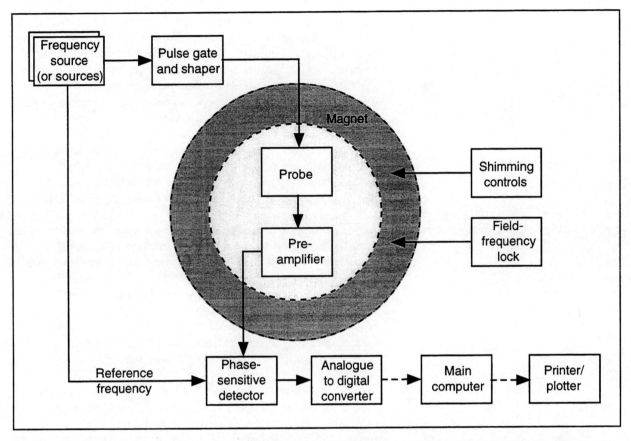

Frequency source (or sources)

Pulse gate and shaper

Magnet

Probe

Shimming controls

Pre-amplifier

Field-frequency lock

Reference frequency

Phase-sensitive detector

Analogue to digital converter

Main computer

Printer/plotter

Block diagram of basic spectrometer components.

precise flip angle and phase (direction in the rotating frame). It may also be necessary to shape the pulses, each pulse building up and dying away in a controlled manner, so that the range of frequencies contained in each pulse can be controlled.

(c) The *magnet and field-frequency lock*. Superconducting magnets, in which the magnetic field is produced by a very large current circulating in a coil of superconducting wire, are almost universally employed; they produce very stable high fields as long as they are regularly topped up with the liquid helium that maintains the coil at a temperature about four kelvins (four degrees above absolute zero). The high-resolution magnet usually produces its field in a vertical room-temperature bore through the centre of the coil, and the sample tube is lowered into the bore on a cushion of compressed air which is also used to keep the sample spinning, where appropriate. Medical NMR magnets tend to have horizontal bores. Machines commonly used for biomolecule work have fields from 6.4 to 14.2 tesla, corresponding to Larmor frequencies from 270 MHz to 600 MHz for protons. The lower end of this range is barely adequate to the task; as frequency rises resolution improves, but almost as importantly so does signal-to-noise. Because the Boltzmann population excess is exponentially related to field strength, the increase of field from 6.4 to 14.2 tesla represents more than eightfold improvement in detectable signal. Further increases in field are on the horizon, but progress is slow and depends on incremental improvements in superconducting technology.

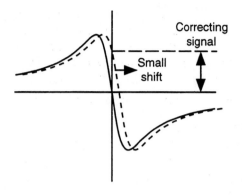

Field-frequency lock: shift in the dispersion-mode deuterium signal produces correcting signal.

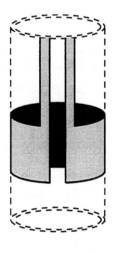

Single-turn probe "coil".

Although the field of a superconducting magnet is naturally very stable, it is not stable enough for NMR where fluctuations of one part in 10^{10} are significant. The field is therefore locked to the frequency of the spectrometer by a *field-frequency lock*. Essentially this means running another NMR experiment in parallel with the main one, usually at the frequency of deuterium, which is a spin-1 nucleus. The deuterium resonance is continuously detected in dispersive mode (see diagram and section 3.5(d)) and the signal at the centre of the resonance continuously monitored. Any drift in field or frequency results in a shift of the resonance, and the monitor channel picks up a non-zero signal which can be used to feed back a correction to the magnet or frequency generator.

As well as being stable over time, the field within an NMR magnet must be uniform – every part of the sample must be in the same field strength. This is achieved by varying the currents in a series of specially designed coils near the sample region. These coils are called shim coils, and the process of adjusting the currents is called shimming. Shimming is normally performed automatically, though few operators can resist a final manual tweak. In some cases the sample itself may affect local magnetic field gradients, so shimming should normally be checked for each new sample.

(d) The *probe*. In Section 2.8 we described how the NMR experiment is conducted by first irradiating the sample with a pulse or pulses of radiofrequency radiation, and then detecting the resultant FID using a small coil placed near the sample. In practice the same coil is used to perform both functions. It is necessary that during the pulse the coil produces a uniform radiofrequency field within the sample: this is best achieved by using a *Helmholtz pair* – a pair of coils with a space between them and carrying identical currents. Single-turn coils suffice at the high frequencies used, so the coil may look like the sketch at left, each turn being deposited or attached to a glass tube which surrounds the sample tube inside the magnet. Painstaking development of probe design has been responsible for much improvement in the sensitivity of NMR instruments over the years.

(e) The *preamplifier*. The tiny FID signal picked up by the probe must be amplified at its original radiofrequency before being passed on for detection. The amplifier which does this must be very efficient and in particular must add very little noise to the already noisy signal before it is amplified further. Along with probe design, good preamplifier design is one of the most important contributions to the construction of an efficient spectrometer.

(f) The *phase-sensitive detector*. The amplified signal from the preamplifier is still at the original Larmor frequency, but we are only interested in the chemical shifts – the small variations of precession frequency, spanning only a few parts per million, between signals from nuclei in different chemical environments. As we have seen, another way of looking at these variations is to see them in the rotating frame of reference; if we specify the frequency at which this is rotating, each separate M_{xy} will be rotating at only a low frequency relative to it. The phase-sensitive detector effectively puts all our measurements into the rotating frame by subtracting the fundamental spectrometer frequency, fed to it directly from the primary frequency source, from the FID signal it receives. Thus a signal passing into the detector at radiofrequency emerges at very much lower (audio) frequencies, measured only in kilohertz. These low-frequency signals are much easier to digitise and to process in every way, but contain *all* the useful information of the original signal. All of the relative frequencies and relative phases of the original components of the FID are thus preserved for analysis.

(g) The *analogue-to-digital converter*. Up to this point in the spectrometer the signal has been an *analogue* signal – continuous variation of voltage in electrical circuits. For computer analysis it must now be converted to an equivalent string of numbers. The analogue-to-digital converter (ADC) performs this task. It must sample the signal at a rate at least twice the highest frequency to be analysed (see diagram, left). Commonly an ADC will convert each sample into a binary number with twelve digits. The biggest number that can be stored in this way is 2^{12}, that is 4096; if the largest value sampled is assigned this value, the smallest will have to be bigger than 1 to be digitised properly. Thus there is a problem with a spectrum which has a large *dynamic range* – where the largest signal in the spectrum is more than 4096 times the size of the smallest. This can readily arise where there is a very large peak in the spectrum from the solvent, invariably present in much higher concentrations than the solute. In such a case the spectrum of the solute may be recorded inefficiently, if at all. This is one reason why suppression of solvent signals is important (see section 3.9).

(h) The computer and displays/plotters. Originally spectrometers had only a single dedicated computer for controlling the experiment and data processing, but it is more common now to separate these roles; data processing can be very computer-intensive and better dealt with by separate offline machines. There is also a move away from purpose-designed NMR-specific computers and towards standard high-performance workstations. Final output on paper requires a large-format (A2 or A1 paper size) plotter, because two-dimensional spectra may be very complex and need to be printed on a large scale for analysis. The plotter is usually accompanied by a laserprinter for quick output of less complex spectra or where large size is not required.

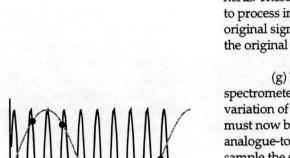

Signal (black line) which is inadequately sampled (•) appears to have incorrect frequency (shaded line). To avoid this, signals must be sampled at least twice per cycle, so sampling rate must always be at least twice the highest frequency required.

3.4 Frequencies, foldback and quadrature detection

The audiofrequency output of the detector is related to the *difference* between the reference radiofrequency ν_0 and the resonance radiofrequencies ν_1 of the nuclei in the sample. In fact the output of the phase-sensitive detector is of the form $cos[2\pi(\nu_0-\nu_1)t+\phi]$ where ϕ

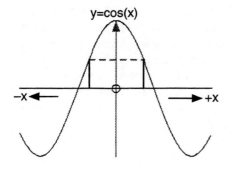

Cosine of x has the same value whether x is positive or negative.

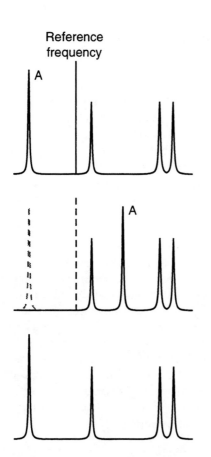

Foldback. If the reference signal (top) is placed within the spectrum, peaks such as A will be folded back into the transformed spectrum (middle). Quadrature detection overcomes the problem (bottom).

is the phase difference between the two frequencies (hence the name phase-sensitive detector). The problem with such an output is that the cosine of a given number is numerically the same whether the number is positive or negative – in other words there is no way of telling whether the Larmor frequency v_1 is larger or smaller than v_0. Some assumption has to be made about this, so in general the experiment may be set up so that the reference (carrier) frequency lies to one side of all the Larmor frequencies of the sample; during Fourier transformation the signals are then all displayed on one side of the reference frequency. This will be done regardless of the sign of (v_0-v_1), so that any signals that *were* to the other side of the pulse frequency will appear in the wrong place – reflected (or *folded back*) about the carrier frequency. The approach provides a simple answer to the sign problem, but it leaves us with another disadvantage. Even if there are no actual *signals* on the "wrong" side of the pulse, there will certainly be noise, and this *does* get folded back into the spectrum. The spectrum thus contains twice as much noise as it should do, worsening the signal to noise ratio by a factor of 1.4.

The commonly used antidote to this problem is to use *two* phase-sensitive detectors. These are both fed the sample signal and a reference frequency as before, but the two reference signals are arranged to be 90° out of phase with each other. The outputs of the two detectors are fed separately to the computer, and in the subsequent Fourier transformation the phase difference between the resulting spectra enables a proper distinction to be drawn between positive and negative frequency differences. The advantages of this are twofold: firstly, noise is not folded back into the spectrum, so that accumulation time is cut by a factor of two, and secondly it is possible to place the pulse transmitter frequency in the centre of the spectrum, making the most efficient use of the radiofrequency pulse power across all the frequencies in the sample.

The process of using two phase sensitive detectors is known as *quadrature detection*, and is routinely used in modern spectrometers. Its success depends critically on the signals reaching the computer being identical except for the phase shift imposed on the reference signal, and so data collection is organised to ensure this, for example by cycling signals alternately through the amplifiers to compensate for any slight differences in gain or amplifier characteristics.

3.5 Data manipulation

Once the FID has been collected and is safely stored in the computer, there are a number of ways in which it needs to be altered to make the NMR spectrum presentable. There are also ways to make the data it contains more accessible or more useful. Standard data-manipulations may be listed as:

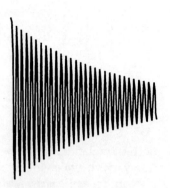

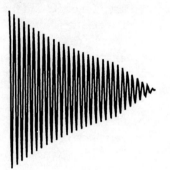

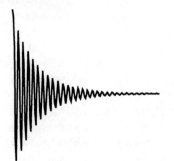

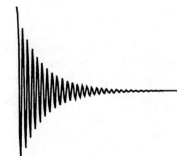

FID's from top to bottom: truncated,
apodised, exponentially multiplied, zero
filled.

(a) Apodisation. The FID usually contains faster-decaying components (usually sample resonances) and slower ones (often solvent resonances). The useful (sample) data is thus mostly collected during the early part of the acquisition time, before the visible FID has completely decayed to zero, and collection may stop at this point. The resultant truncated shape of the FID will cause the spectrum after transformation to be distorted, with the solvent peaks in particular dipping below the baseline; the solvent line-shape is a hybrid between Lorentzian and sinc functions. To minimise the sinc component, which is the one which causes the dip below the baseline, data processing will normally include *apodisation* – multiplication of the final part of the FID by some function that decays more gently to zero.

(b) Exponential multiplication. The FID contains both signal (from M_{xy}) and noise. Since the signal is decaying and the noise is not, the early part of the FID has a better signal-to-noise ratio than the later part. We can thus improve the overall signal-to-noise ratio in the transformed spectrum by de-emphasising the later part: this may be achieved by multiplying the FID by an exponentially decreasing function. Of course you never get something for nothing; the cost of this improvement comes in the fact that we are artificially reducing the apparent T_2, and so will get a spectrum with better signal-to-noise but with broadened lines. Multiplication in this way is technically a process of *convolution*. The converse process also works – by reducing the apparent rate of decay of the FID by multiplying it by an exponentially increasing function, we get a sharper spectrum with a (much) poorer noise level. This is *deconvolution*.

(c) Zero-filling. The FID as collected is of course stored in digital form: an array of numbers representing samples of the real FID taken during its decay. The number of data points is determined by the rate of sampling (at least twice the highest frequency in the NMR spectrum) and by the length of time for which the FID was collected. The fast transformation then yields two versions of the NMR spectrum in the computer; these are mathematically the real and imaginary results of the transformation, and can be manipulated to correspond to the absorption and dispersion mode spectra first described by Bloch. These spectra contain equivalent information, but each occupies only half the data points of the original input FID. Plotting just one of them may then result in a spectrum which lacks detail simply because not enough data points

were available to display all the available information. To obtain more points, the FID could be sampled faster or for a longer time. Alternatively, we may *zero-fill* the data – add zeros to the FID before transforming it, and so obtain a spectrum with more data points. This isn't cheating by inventing data points – rather it is the most efficient use of the data set, as well as providing a better-looking final spectrum.

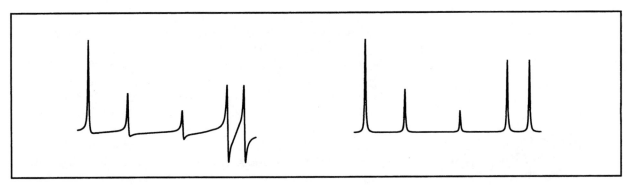

Left: spectrum with phase errors; right: after correction.

(d) Phase correction. The Bloch formulation shows that the lineshape of the transformed spectrum varies between the absorption mode and the dispersion mode according to the *phase relationship* between a given frequency component of the FID and the applied radiofrequency field B_1. This phase relationship may vary through the spectrum, and is not automatically calculated or corrected during the Fourier transformation. If the lineshapes of the final spectrum are not to be distorted, phase correction (either manually by the operator or automatically by the computer) must be applied after the transformation. Correction will normally be required for two phase errors: a (zero-order) phase error that is constant across the whole spectrum and another (first-order) that varies linearly from one end of the spectrum to the other.

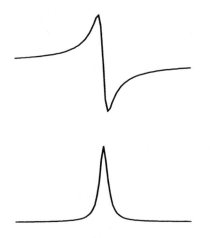

Transformed spectral line: Above, dispersion mode; below, absorption mode

(e) Resolution enhancement and spectrum optimisation. Much effort has gone into finding more sophisticated ways to modify the shape of a FID before transformation to get the best possible compromise between resolution and noise. What is needed is a modifying function which will combine the best features of convolution (improvement of signal-to-noise) and deconvolution (improvement of resolution). A number of functions are available for altering the shape of the FID. These include a *gaussian function*, the application of which sharpens the lines by converting them from the Lorentzian lineshape with broad "wings" at its base to a Gaussian shape which drops more abruptly to the baseline. Also popular are *double-exponentials* (an increasing exponential followed by a decreasing one) and *sinebell functions* which are shaped as portions of a sinewave. The rationale for all these functions is that they de-emphasise the first few points of the FID, which can sometimes be corrupted and cause spectral distortions, and the later points in the FID which contribute disproportionately low signal-to-noise (see (d) above). Commercial NMR software invariably provides for the application of a variety of such functions, either automatically or interactively.

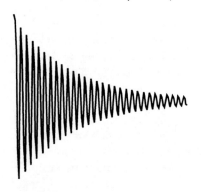

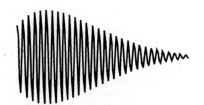

Top: normal FID; bottom: after multiplication with a sinebell function.

3.6 Maximum entropy methods

The fast-Fourier-transform algorithm is fast and not too demanding of computer power, but it is subject to a number of drawbacks which can lead to distortions in the spectrum, particularly if a few data points are corrupted or the dataset is truncated. A method which requires far more computation, but can offer superior results, has been used successfully in a number of applications – the *maximum entropy* method, often known as MEM or Maxent. Perhaps best known in applications such as the deblurring of photographic images, a requirement of the method is that the form of the blurring is known; in other words that some information is available concerning the nature of the data if it were noise-free. In the case of NMR spectra this input would be the lineshape and linewidth anticipated for the sample. The MEM algorithm then attempts to find the smallest amount of spectral information compatible with the observed data. In effect, it seeks for the spectrum which is the *most probable* member of an enormous family of spectra which are all compatible with the input data. Along with the most probable result, the maximum entropy method provides a number which can be regarded as a *quality factor*. If different input lineshapes or linewidths produce a spectrum with a higher quality factor, then that spectrum is a better fit to the data. Although MEM cannot put in data that is not there in the first place, it can reveal what is there with better resolution and lower noise than Fourier transformation, and because of the probabilistic nature of its calculations it also permits the estimation of errors in numerical results such as J-couplings. Maximum entropy methods work best when applied to data in which the linewidths of all the peaks are closely similar.

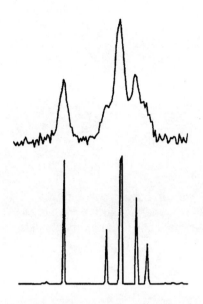

Original data (top) optimally analysed by the maximum entropy method (bottom). (Spectra reproduced by courtesy of MaxEnt Solutions Ltd.)

3.7 Measurement of relaxation times

3.7.1 Measurement of T_2 using spin echoes

[handwritten: Mxy component]

[handwritten: Resultant magnetisation M has components in Mz and Mxy plane]

T_2 may be measured by a 'spin-echo' experiment, which may take one of several forms. A 90° pulse tips the magnetisation into the xy plane and is then followed by an exponential decay of M_{xy} which occurs in two ways:

[handwritten: phase coherence]

(a) by *normal transverse relaxation*, an irreversible process caused by magnetic noise and spin exchange.

(b) by loss of phase coherence through *magnetic-field inhomogeneities*. Different parts of the sample are in slightly different applied magnetic fields due to imperfections in the instrument's magnet. Their M_{xy} components thus precess at slightly different frequencies, and signals from chemically identical nuclei in different parts of the field are seen to 'fan out' in the rotating frame. Slower-

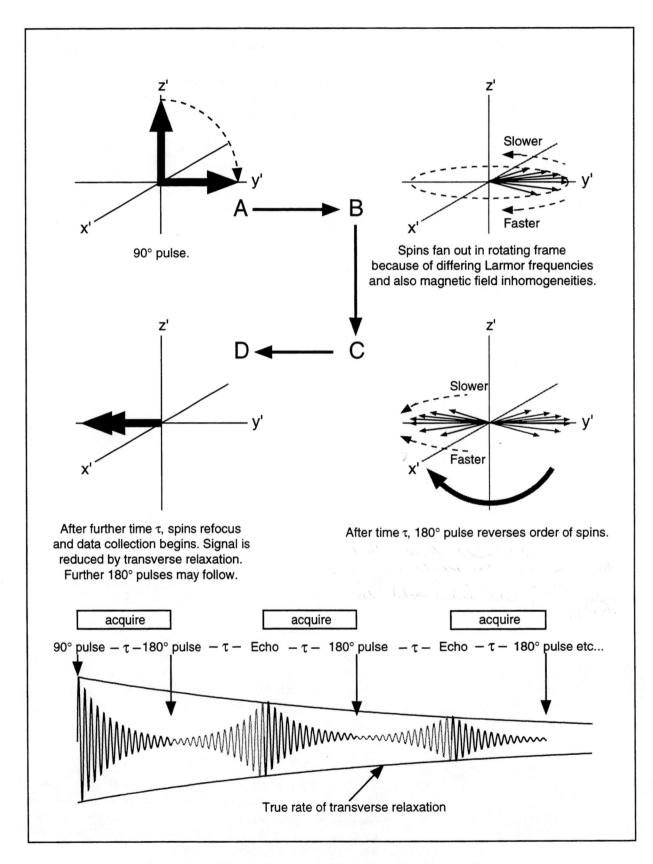

Spin-echo method for measuring transverse relaxation time T$_2$.

precessing spins fall behind, faster ones move ahead. Note that this effect, which is always present because no magnetic field is ever perfectly homogeneous, contributes to the apparent T_2 of all nuclei. This apparent T_2, as seen in the decay of the FID and the linewidths of the spectrum after transformation, is often called T_2* to distinguish it from the true transverse relaxation time.

At a time τ after the 90° pulse, a 180° pulse is applied. Whether it is applied along the x´ axis or the y´ axis in the rotating frame, the effect is the same: the order of the spins is reversed, with the slower ones now ahead (and falling back) and the faster ones behind (and catching up). The spins which were dephasing due to field inhomogeneity are now *regaining* their phase coherence at the same rate as they lost it. At the end of another time τ they come together again, their signal reaches a maximum and a *spin-echo* is detected. But only the systematic dephasing (b) is reversible by this process; true transverse relaxation (a), which is a random process, is not reversed and so the 'echo' is smaller than the original signal. The process may be repeated: at time τ after the echo (and 2τ after the first 180° pulse) another 180° pulse will reverse things again and give rise to another, smaller echo. Thus a series of echoes is formed, the decay rate of which will reveal the true transverse relaxation time. This is the *Carr-Purcell* pulse sequence.

Although the process works whether the 180° pulses are in the same phase as the original 90° pulse or not, it was later shown that problems due to inhomogeneities in the radiofrequency (B_1) field were minimised if they were out of phase; in other words, if a $90°_x$ pulse (a 90° pulse directed along the x´ axis in the rotating frame) were followed by a series of $180°_y$ pulses (directed along the y´ axis). This then constitutes the *Carr-Purcell-Meiboom-Gill* pulse sequence.

3.7.2 Measurement of T_1 by inversion recovery. M_z component

T_1 may be measured by applying a series of pulse sequences of the type 180°-τ-90°, where τ is a small time which is varied from one pulse sequence to the next. The first, 180°, pulse inverts M_z, which then decays exponentially towards its original value. After time τ the magnetisation will have relaxed to a value M which may be measured by applying a 90° pulse (as in a normal NMR experiment), which tips it into the xy plane so that it can be detected. A series of FID's, corresponding to different values of τ, are accumulated and transformed. In the resulting set of 'partially relaxed' spectra, the size of each individual peak is a function of its own T_1 value. The diagram (overleaf) shows a series of such partially relaxed spectra: a plot of the natural logarithm of peak height against τ will give an accurate value of T_1 for each resonance. A rough T_1 may also be found from the fact that the value of τ for which M passes through zero is given by $\tau=0.69T_1$.

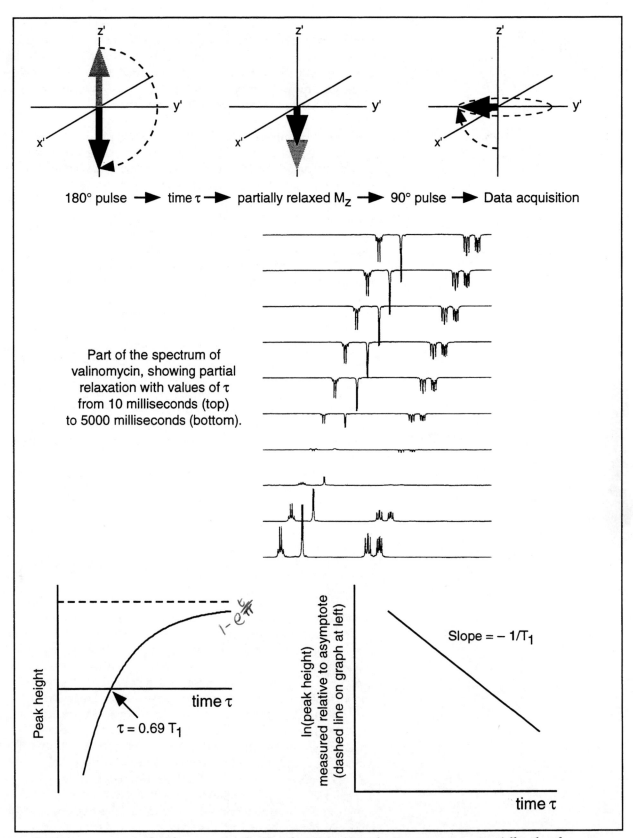

180° pulse ➡ time τ ➡ partially relaxed M$_z$ ➡ 90° pulse ➡ Data acquisition

Part of the spectrum of valinomycin, showing partial relaxation with values of τ from 10 milliseconds (top) to 5000 milliseconds (bottom).

Inversion-recovery method for measuring T$_1$. Top, the 180°-τ-90° pulse sequence; centre, partially relaxed spectra; bottom, graphs of individual peak heights used to give value of T$_1$.

3.8 Paramagnetic effects in NMR

Many biological investigations using NMR, particularly in the earlier days of the technique, have used paramagnetic ions as probes. The unpaired electron of such an ion has a magnetic dipole moment nearly 2000 times greater than that of a proton, and can induce chemical shift changes of 20-40 ppm and/or significant broadening of the resonances from nuclei neighbouring the paramagnetic centre. Interpretation of the perturbed spectra should give valuable information on the geometry of the system, as the paramagnetic effects are highly anisotropic; such interpretation is often not easy.

Interaction of a nucleus with an unpaired electron is similar to that between two nuclei - it may be:

(a) A direct dipole-dipole interaction. This is a direct interaction between two vectors, and the effect is directional. If there is a time-invariant component to the interaction, it will generate a chemical shift which is known as a *pseudocontact shift*. Time-dependent fluctuation of the interaction will produce line-broadening effects through *dipolar relaxation*.

(b) An indirect coupling which depends on the extent to which an unpaired electron dwells at a given nucleus. This is not directional; if it has a time-invariant component a chemical shift (Fermi shift or *contact shift*) is produced. Time-dependent fluctuations will produce *scalar relaxation*.

In a real situation not all of these four effects may be significant; if one of them dominates it makes interpretation of the spectra much easier. However, the situation is further complicated by the fact that an electron has an orbital magnetic moment as well as a spin magnetic moment; its total magnetic moment is the sum of the two. Orbital magnetic moments do not lend themselves to calculation except in the very simplest cases - indeed, they are dependent to an extent on the environment of the ion. As a result, the theoretical treatment of paramagnetic effects is complicated by the large number of assumptions that have to be built into the equations. This has not prevented excellent and quantitative work being done.

The uses of paramagnetic reagents as probes of structure fall into five classes:

1. Solvent proton relaxation enhancement (PRE) produced by paramagnetic ions in solutions of macromolecules

2. Enhanced relaxation of nuclei in substrates or inhibitors bound to macromolecules

3. Intrinsic shift probes (i.e. naturally occurring paramagnetic centres) in metalloproteins, particularly haem proteins

4. Paramagnetic ions, especially lanthanides, as extrinsic shift and relaxation probes for both small and large molecules, for example the substitution of a paramagnetic ion such as manganese or a lanthanide for the magnesium ion in lysozyme

5. Spin labels (stable organic free radicals) as relaxation probes.

Although paramagnetic probe experiments can be very powerful and quantitative, the applications of isotopic labelling and multi-dimensional spectroscopy described in Chapters 4 and 5 have proved so fruitful that paramagnetics have rather fallen into disuse in recent years. For a fuller and very clear account of this topic, the reader is referred to Jardetzky and Roberts "NMR in Molecular Biology" which is listed in the Bibliography.

3.9 Spectroscopy in water

Nearly all the original proton NMR work on biological molecules was performed in heavy water (D_2O) solution. This is because the concentration of protons in normal water is so much greater than that of solute molecules (which are normally at millimolar concentrations) that it is effectively impossible to digitise both at the same time; the dynamic range is too great for the analogue-to-digital converter. A water peak may be 100,000 time the size of a solute peak. Use of D_2O, which contains only a few residual protons, overcomes this problem, and incidentally provides a deuterium NMR signal which can be used for the field-frequency lock of the spectrometer. The disadvantage of D_2O as a solvent is that exchangeable protons of the solute molecules exchange with deuterons from the solvent, and so no NH or COOH proton resonances are visible in the spectrum unless some factor prevents them from exchanging. Low pH, participation in a hydrogen bond, or being buried inside a large molecule may prevent hydrogen-deuterium exchange, and this is of course itself a source of interesting observations.

More recently, however, it has become essential to record all the possible data from a sample, including that from exchangeable protons, and hence to run samples in ordinary water solution. This need has been met by the development of a variety of ways of suppressing the solvent peak, so that it is now routine not only to keep within the desirable dynamic range, but also to avoid the problem of very large solvent resonances effectively blanking out large regions of the spectrum. Several alternative methods exist:

(a) Saturation. The result of prolonged irradiation of a sample at the Larmor frequency of the water resonance is to cause so many transitions between the allowed states that the Boltzmann population difference is temporarily lost. When a 90° pulse is then applied to the sample, there is no M_Z for the water resonance, and

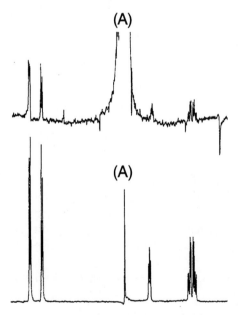

(A)

(A)

Reduction of water peak intensity by presaturation of the water resonance (A): top, unsuppressed; bottom, with suppression. Note the improved signal to noise in the lower spectrum resulting from more efficient digitisation of sample resonances once water is suppressed.

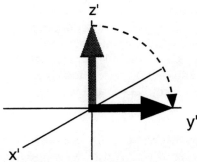

90°$_{+x}$ pulse for all spins.
Reference (carrier) frequency is set
to be same as solvent resonance.

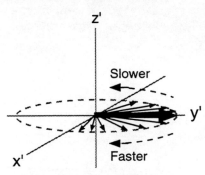

Spins fan out in rotating frame
because of differing Larmor
frequencies. Solvent spins stay
in y' direction.

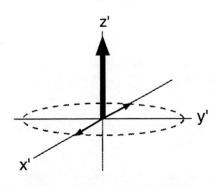

90°$_{-x}$ pulse returns solvent spins to z
axis, where they are undetectable. y'
components of sample are also lost,
but x' components remain to be
detected.

*The jump-and return sequence for solvent
suppression.*

thus no detectable M_{xy} after the pulse. The method works, but suffers from the disadvantage that any protons which are in rapid chemical exchange with the water will also be affected. It is possible that future solvent suppression will rely on the application of a fast-switched *field gradient* following a solvent-selective 90° pulse; such a gradient effectively dephases solvent spins from different parts of the sample, completely removing the net solvent M_{xy} and M_z and providing a very rapid route to solvent saturation without attendant chemical-exchange problems.

(b) Inversion recovery. A 180° pulse is applied to the sample. Water has a long T_1, and a delay time is programmed so that the water protons undergo longitudinal relaxation until the point at which their resultant M_z is just passing through zero. By this time the resonances of the sample will have fully relaxed, so at this point a 90° pulse will produce a normal spectrum with the water suppressed. This works well provided the 180° pulse is uniform throughout the sample, a condition that is not always easy to meet.

(c) Jump-and return. In this method, the transmitter (pulse) frequency is set at the water resonance so that the water M_{xy} is stationary in the rotating frame. A 90° pulse is applied in the +x´ direction, and after a short delay an identical pulse is applied in the -x´ direction. In the rotating frame, the water resonance will have stayed along the y´ axis during the delay, and will simply be flipped back into the z direction, producing no detectable signal. Resonances at other frequencies, however, which are not stationary in the rotating frame, will have fanned out from the y´ direction during the delay time, and the second 90° pulse will not remove all their M_{xy} magnetisation; they will thus give rise to detectable signals. Of course, the effective flip angle of these resonances will vary with their distance from the water resonance, but this can be corrected, as can the 180° phase difference between resonances on opposite sides of the water frequency.

(d) Binomial pulse sequences. These are a more complex form of solvent suppression in which a train of pulses with systematically varied flip angles and directions is applied. The flip angles follow a binomial distribution. In particular the 1, -2,1 sequence and the 1,-3,3,-1 sequences are often used, with a basic flip angle of perhaps $\pi/16$. Thus a 1,-3,3,1 sequence might be $(\pi/16)_x$, $(3\pi/16)_{-x}$, $(3\pi/16)_x$, $(\pi/16)_{-x}$. The result is the same as the jump-and-return, in that very little or no solvent M_{xy} results, while solvent M_z is almost at its equilibrium value while data is collected.

Of the above methods, the pulse methods are by and large preferred to saturation, with the choice between jump-and-return and binomial sequences (or variants thereon) being determined by the capabilities of the particular machine, ease of setting up or the requirements of a particular sample. There are two other ways of removing solvent peaks from spectra:

(e) Post-accumulation data processing. In addition to the experimental methods outlined above, a number of computer-based statistical methods exist which permit the reduction of solvent resonances. These include statistical methods which extract the strong, highly correlated solvent signal and thus permit its subtraction from the weaker, uncorrelated sample signals, and other methods which rely on deconvolution.

(f) Multiple-quantum experiments. Quite a number of more sophisticated NMR experiments use double- or multiple-quantum coherences (Chapters 4 and 5) which give signals only from nuclei which are spin-coupled within a system of at least two spins. Such double- or multiple-quantum-filtered (DQF or MQF) experiments, while performed primarily for the extra information they can provide, incidentally produce spectra that are entirely free of solvent peaks.

3.10 One-dimensional NMR of large molecules – problems and solutions

Any successful NMR experiment comes in three stages:

1. *Resolve the resonances* – that is, obtain a spectrum in which the signals are clearly distinguished from one another, and with the minimum of interference from noise.

2. *Assign the resonances.* Each resonance peak comes from a particular chemical environment within the molecule – but which? Assigning each resonance to a particular atom in a molecule is the heart of the spectroscopist's task: it can be a very long and difficult process.

3. *Interpret the data.* As ever, if the experiment is well designed and the data is good, this is the fun part.

In chapters 4 and 5 we shall cover ways in which 2D and 3D methods have made major inroads into the resolution and assignment problems for biological molecules; nevertheless one-dimensional spectroscopy has ways of overcoming them too, and these deserve a brief examination:

3.10.1 Resolving the resonances.

Many potentially good NMR experiments on large molecules have never passed this stage, largely because of:

(a) *Signal-to-noise problems.* Despite many improvements in the design of NMR spectrometers over the years, the small population difference between upper and lower energy levels means that NMR remains inherently an insensitive technique. The chief way of overcoming this is by signal averaging , as described earlier. But it remains true that solution NMR of large molecules is only possible using concentrations many times that found in vivo, and not all molecules are sufficiently soluble or well behaved at such high concentrations.

(b) *Overlapping resonances*. Large molecules give large numbers of resonances, but because large molecules are also slow moving they have long correlation times, short T_2's and broad resonances. As the molecules get bigger, the resonances are more numerous; they are also broader and the combination of these two factors means that the one-dimensional spectrum of a large molecule consists of overlapped resonances, burying the data under broad featureless humps. This is depressing, but much less of a problem with two- and three- dimensional NMR.

There are many ways of approaching the resolution problem in one-dimensional spectra: a few of the very many strategies which can be adopted are:

(i) Get time on a higher-frequency spectrometer. Linewidths and J-values are constant when measured in Hz, while chemical shifts are proportional to the applied field. Thus working at a higher field effectively makes the lines narrower on a parts-per-million scale with the added bonus that complex second-order spin-spin splitting patterns may be simplified to first-order. Current commercial spectrometers operate between 100 and 600 MHz (750 MHz is on the horizon): for serious work with large molecules, at least 4-500 MHz is essential.

(ii) Use resonances whose chemical shifts are naturally clear of the rest of the spectrum; special favourites have been the CH resonances of the imidazole ring of histidine, and ring-current shifted resonances moved clear of the rest of the spectrum by proximity to a tyrosine, tryptophan or phenylalanine sidechain.

(iii) Chemically, or otherwise, label the molecule with NMR-active nuclei which are not naturally present. An example might be to label (at a known site) with a trifluoroacetyl group and then look at the ^{19}F spectrum, which will only then have one resonance. Designing an experiment in which this probe can be persuaded to give biochemically meaningful information is an interesting challenge.

(iv) Use isotopic labelling, either positive or negative. Positive labelling is exemplified by labelling selected sites in a molecule with carbon-13. Since ^{13}C constitutes only just over one percent of natural carbon, ^{13}C resonances from the labelled sites will dominate the carbon spectrum, and be easier to assign as well. An example of negative labelling would be to deuterate the molecule (i.e. replace all the hydrogen atoms with deuterium) leaving selected groups protonated, so only those groups will show up in the proton

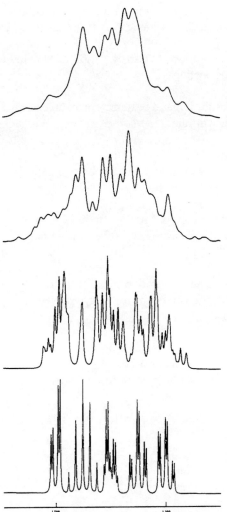

Effect of increasing spectrometer frequency. Top to bottom: 60, 270, 400, 600 MHz. As well as permitting all the peaks to be resolved, the highest frequency simplifies the spectrum to first-order so that the spin couplings are readily analysed.

spectrum. Experiments with isotopic labelling of this kind were first performed in the 1970's, but proved very difficult and expensive; widespread application had to await the recombinant DNA revolution, and the development of expression systems which permit overproduction of proteins from organisms with simple nutritional requirements (see Chapter 5).

(v) Use difference spectroscopy, for example between metalloenzymes with paramagnetic and diamagnetic ions at the metal centre.

(vi) Use data-manipulation methods to narrow, and hence help to resolve, the resonances (see Section 3.3).

Despite the problems of resolution and assignment, even one-dimensional NMR, properly applied, has some unique advantages. Among them are:

(i) it can be very specific – for example, you can observe the pK_a of a single histidine residue in a large protein.

(ii) it works in solution, which means that the effects of variables such as pH, temperature and substrate concentration can be monitored.

(iii) it provides a valuable parallel to (and in some cases, check on) x-ray crystallographic data, and can of course be applied to molecules that do not crystallise.

(iv) it can provide information on molecular motion through measurements of relaxation times T_1 and T_2 and by observation of exchange and other effects. Dynamic measurements are discussed in Section 6.1.

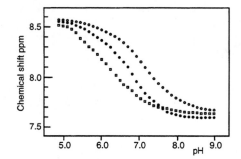

Resonances from individual histidines within a protein shift with pH, revealing pK values.

CHAPTER 4: A SECOND DIMENSION

New pathways to resolution, assignment, and molecular structure.

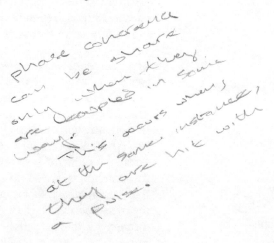

4.1 Introduction.

The central problem for the NMR of large molecules using one-dimensional NMR is that of overlapping data. All the chemical shift and other information is present, but inaccessible. It is as if the words on this page were all to be printed on the same line – the resulting almost-solid black would be impossible to read. The way to make the words readable is to spread them out in two dimensions on the page, and the same applies to NMR. By spreading the resonances out to form a map, the resolution of the data is remarkably improved. To understand the process we need consider only two new foundation ideas.

The first four lines of this chapter printed on top of each other.

4.2 Foundation idea 1: Phase coherence can be exchanged

The detection of NMR depends entirely on the magnetisation M_{xy}, which is the resultant of the xy components of all the nuclear spins in the sample that share an identical chemical environment. Each spin may be in a separate molecule, each undergoes its own randomly determined relaxation processes, but collectively, because of their *phase coherence*, these freely-precessing spins generate a macroscopic rotating magnetisation which reveals their Larmor frequency and transverse relaxation time, exhibited as chemical shift and linewidth in the Fourier-transformed spectrum. What is not evident from this 'classical' picture (it only becomes clear in the mathematics of a quantum-mechanical treatment) is that under appropriate circumstances the phase coherence of one group of spins, complete with its phase information, *can be passed on to another group.* Further, the second group need not even be nuclei of the same element; if the experiment is properly designed, phase

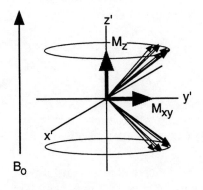

Mxy revisited - see Chapter 2.

coherence that has been induced in a group of protons that share a Larmor frequency can be passed on to a group of similarly-related carbon-13 nuclei, even though the precession frequency of carbon is only a quarter of that of protons in the same magnetic field.

The transfer of phase coherence can be achieved experimentally in a number of ways, but always subject to one condition: transfer is only possible between spins which are *coupled* in some way. In practice this means that phase coherence can be transferred in only two circumstances: either between spins that are joined through a few covalent bonds, so that they exhibit spin-spin (scalar) coupling with each other, or between spins that, although not connected through bonds, are so close to each other in space (in practice, less than 0.5 nm apart) that they continuously exchange their nuclear magnetisation through direct interaction between their dipole moments. Different pulse sequences can be used to cause coherence transfer in the two cases. If an experiment using the appropriate pulse sequence does demonstrate a transfer of phase coherence between groups of spins, that transfer is evidence of their through-bond or through-space connectedness.

Coherence-transfer (sometimes called magnetisation-transfer) experiments constitute an enormous leap forward on the one-dimensional NMR outlined in Chapters 2 and 3. Firstly, they allow the resonances to be spread out in two or more dimensions, effectively ending the problem of overlapping data. Secondly, the unambiguous demonstration of connectedness through bonds vastly simplifies the problem of resonance assignment (i.e. changes it from almost-impossible to merely very-difficult-indeed). Thirdly, the identification of many through-space contacts has made the full structural analysis of very complex molecules such as moderately sized proteins possible. Fourthly, because many of the coherences used in the experiment are detected only indirectly, it is possible to exploit a large number of so-called *forbidden transitions* which can never be directly detected, but which nevertheless contribute valuable information. Finally, (though the list could go on) the power of NMR to investigate dynamic processes in molecules is greatly extended by coherence-transfer methods.

The remaining question is how coherence transfer may be detected; the answer lies in *frequency labelling*.

Relaxed spin system

$\downarrow$

Pulse causes spins
to precess coherently

$\downarrow$

After a short time, second pulse
transfers coherence
to second group of spins

$\downarrow$

Data is collected from
second group of spins

The basic processes which lead to a 2D spectrum.

4.3 Foundation idea 2: Frequency labelling

Consider a sample in which the only NMR-active nuclei are all in identical chemical environments. There is thus only one Larmor frequency (v_1) and only one peak in the NMR spectrum. If we apply a 90° pulse along the x axis, the net magnetisation Mz is tipped into the +y direction, and begins to precess in the xy plane at frequency v_1. If we now wait for a time t_1 (not to be confused with

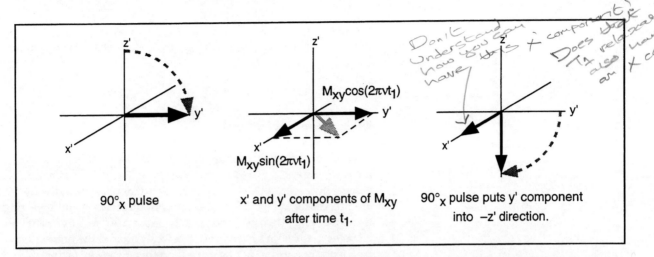

handwritten: Don't understand how you can have this x component? Does this x relaxation T₁ also have an x component?

$M_{xy}cos(2\pi v t_1)$

$M_{xy}sin(2\pi v t_1)$

90°ₓ pulse

x' and y' components of M_{xy} after time t_1.

90°ₓ pulse puts y' component into –z' direction.

*(Above) 90° – t_1 – 90° pulse sequence for 2D frequency labelling.
(Below) transformed peak for different values of t_1, with (bottom) plot of points marked •.*

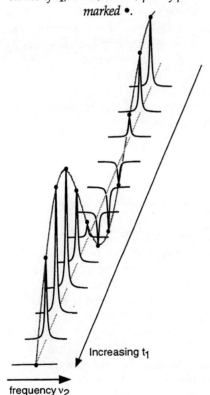

Increasing t_1

frequency v_2

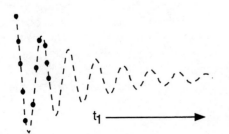

t_1 ⟶

longitudinal relaxation time T_1) this M_{xy} magnetisation will have precessed through an angle $2\pi v_1 t_1$, the product of angular velocity and time. Ignoring for the moment that the magnetisation will also have decayed a little (determined by T_2^*) during this time, it will now have components $M_{xy}cos(2\pi v_1 t_1)$ along the y'-axis and $M_{xy}sin(2\pi v_1 t_1)$ along the x-axis (see diagram above).

If we now apply a *second* 90° pulse along the x'-axis, the y'-component of M_{xy} will be tilted into the minus-z' direction, where it becomes undetectable and will simply undergo longitudinal relaxation through zero and back to its equilibrium value. The x'-component, however, is unaffected by the pulse and continues to precess. The size of the signal we now detect thus depends on the size of the x-component, which is $M_{xy}sin(2\pi v_1 t_1)$ and thus depends on t_1 and the Larmor frequency v_1 of the nuclei. This means that the initial size of the signal detected after the 90° pulse is effectively a *label* of the frequency of precession v_1 during time t_1. We collect the FID of this signal over a period of time which we call the *acquisition time* t_2.

We now repeat this experiment a number of times, increasing t_1 for each successive FID. Typically we might collect data for 256 or 512 different values of t_1, with each FID digitised into 256 or 512 data points. The result is a *matrix* of data, each row of which is one FID. If we Fourier transform each row, we get a series of spectra such as those shown in the diagram at left. Being the Fourier transform of a function varying with time (t_2), each spectrum is a plot of intensity against frequency – we call this frequency v_2.

If we look at the data after this first transformation, the size of the one peak in our spectrum varies with t_1, depending on the value of $M_{xy}sin(2\pi v_1 t_1)$. Thus each column of data in the matrix (for example the one that corresponds to the points (•) at the top of the NMR peak) represents a sinusoidal variation at frequency v_1. If we plot this out it looks like another FID (indeed it decays at a rate determined by T_2^*), although strictly not one. If we perform a Fourier transform down that column, we again get a plot of

handwritten: Don't understand labelling

handwritten: (magnitude?)

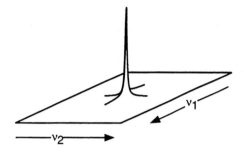

Peak-in-the-middle.

against frequency, this time frequency ν_1. A two-dimensional plot of the whole matrix of data now gives us a single peak – it is at point (ν_2,ν_1) and since

$$\nu_2=\nu_1=\text{the Larmor frequency } \nu$$

it is in the centre of the plot.

In itself, all that this particular experiment has achieved is to measure the Larmor frequency twice over. The value of the method is seen, however, when we consider a situation in which the nuclei are precessing at DIFFERENT Larmor frequencies ν_1 and ν_2 during times t_1 and t_2. This could occur if the second 90° pulse caused changes in the spin system which actually altered the precession frequency of a group of nuclei, or (and this is the key factor) if it caused *phase coherence that had been associated with a group of nuclei precessing at frequency ν_1 during time t_1 to be transferred to a second group of nuclei, precessing at frequency ν_2, which would provide the detected FID during time t_2.* The resonances from these nuclei will then appear on the two-dimensional plot at a point (ν_2,ν_1) where ν_1 represents the precession frequency of the phase coherence during time t_1 and ν_2 that during t_2. The FID is *collected* at frequency ν_2, but it is also *labelled* with frequency ν_1, and the two Fourier transforms reveal this fact. This idea is the basis of all 2D experiments – there are many variants, some very subtle, which differ in the way the two different frequencies are produced and in the information contained in the two-dimensional plot.

4.4 The basic 2D pulse sequence

Some of the pulse sequences used in 2D, 3D (and even 4D) spectroscopy are extremely complicated, with many pulses of different frequencies, flip angles and phases. Successive spectra collected for averaging may also be collected following different pulse sequences which cycle through a pattern of alternating phases to help cancel out artifacts (see page 56). All of these experiments conform to the same basic pattern of four stages: *preparation, evolution, mixing,* and *acquisition.* In the *preparation* phase, the spin systems are set up for the experiment proper; more often than not, this simply means allowing the system enough time to relax to equilibrium, and then applying a 90° pulse to introduce some phase coherence. This is allowed to develop for a time t_1 during the *evolution* period, which is followed by another pulse or pulses. Transfer of phase coherence ensues during the *mixing* period; this is usually ended by another pulse, and the resulting FID collected during the *acquisition* time t_2. 3D experiments are constructed by the addition of a second evolution time and mixing time, and 4D by the addition of yet another (see Chapter 5).

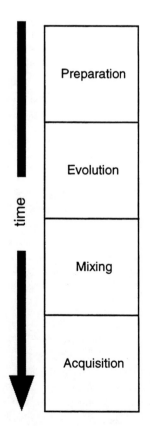

Four stages of a two-dimensional NMR experiment – see text.

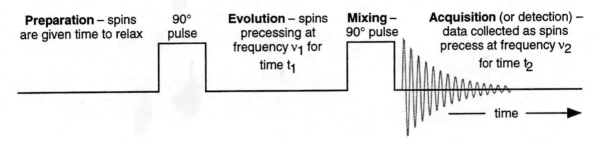

A two-dimensional COSY experiment – basic pulse sequence.

4.5 COSY (COrrelated SpectrocopY)

4.5.1 A thought experiment.

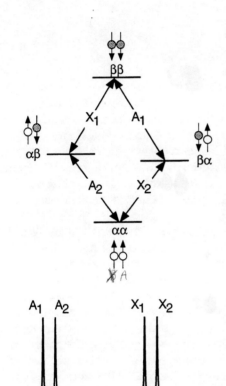

Energy levels and spectrum for two coupled nuclei A and X.

Imagine a two-spin system in which the spins have very different chemical shifts but are spin-coupled to each other (an AX system). Given that each spin may be in one of two states, high or low energy, the system has four possible energies. If we draw an energy level diagram, representing the lower energy state of a single nucleus by α and the upper state by β, we may represent the system by a diagram as at left. The middle two energy levels are very slightly different, so that the four transitions A_1, A_2, X_1, X_2 are all at slightly different frequencies. There are four peaks (two doublets) in the spectrum of this sample; because the populations of the four energy states are *almost* equal, all the peaks will appear to have the same intensity. Suppose a 90° pulse is now applied *to one transition only* (say A_1). To achieve this, the pulse will have to be a *soft* pulse – long (to restrict its frequency spread so that it only excites A_1) and weak (otherwise such a long pulse would tilt M_z through far more than 90°). The result of this pulse is that a quarter of the available spins in the sample (half of the A spins, that is the A spins in half of the sample molecules) are precessing in phase with each other at the frequency corresponding to transition A_1. In this illustrative experiment there is no phase coherence (i.e. no M_{xy}) corresponding to any of the other transitions.

After an evolution time t_1, we apply a second 90° pulse, this time a *hard* pulse which affects all four transitions equally. The effect of this can only be fully explained in quantum-mechanical terms, but its result is that *the original (A_1) phase coherence is shared out among all four energy states*. The second pulse accomplishes the whole of the mixing step of the standard pulse sequence (effectively the mixing time is zero), and *coherence transfer* takes place; the magnetisation that was precessing at the frequency of A_1 for the evolution period is now shared equally between magnetisations precessing at A_1, A_2, X_1, and X_2 frequencies. It may help in understanding this to remember that not only are the spins of the AX system spin-coupled to each other, but also, although they appear far apart in the NMR spectrum, in absolute terms they have *very* similar

Larmor frequencies (differing only by a few parts per million) and therefore classically can share their energy through resonance effects.

After the second pulse, then, instead of only A_1 spins having phase coherence, there is some coherence (i.e. some M_{xy}) corresponding to all the four transitions. If we collect the FID during time t_2, it will contain the Larmor frequencies of all four lines. However, all of them were precessing at the frequency of A_1 during time t_1, and their intensity is thus "labelled" with that frequency. Thus in the two-dimensional plot, four peaks will appear, at frequencies A_1,A_2,X_1,X_2 on the ν_2 axis, but all at the frequency of A_1 in the ν_1 direction.

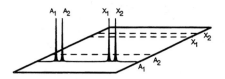

Two-dimensional COSY spectrum with spins labelled at frequency A_1.

4.5.2 A real experiment.

To perform the above experiment in practice, we do not start with a soft 90° pulse, but with a hard pulse which excites all four transitions at the same time. The second pulse still causes sharing of coherence between all the transitions, so the final data set will contain all possible combinations: peaks which precess at A_1 during t_1 and X_1 during t_2, at A_2 during t_1 and A_1 during t_2, at the same frequency during both... – given all the possible combinations, a total of sixteen peaks will appear on the two-dimensional plot.

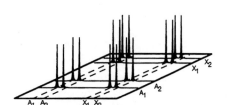

Sixteen peaks resulting from frequency labelling at all four frequencies.

If there had been no coupling between the spins, but just four unrelated resonances which happened to have frequencies A_1, A_2, X_1, and X_2, there would have been no coherence sharing. In such a case only four peaks would have appeared on the 2D spectrum, and they would have been at positions (A_1,A_1), (A_2,A_2), (X_1,X_1) and (X_2,X_2) – in other words, on the *diagonal* of the two-dimensional plot. The presence of off-diagonal peaks (often known as *crosspeaks*) *demonstrates* the spin coupling between A and X. The crosspeaks will still appear even if the actual resonances of A and X are buried under many other peaks on the diagonal of the plot; there is no further need to resolve them. The existence of a crosspeak at point (ν_1, ν_2) on the two-dimensional plot thus tells us three things: (a) there is a resonance at ν_1; (b) there is a resonance at ν_2; and (c) they are coupled to each other. We have a method that will show the existence of all the spin couplings in a sample, no matter how complex the spectrum, and at the same time reveal all the resonances in the sample, whether or not they are resolved in the one-dimensional spectrum, and provided only that they are coupled to something else. Note (and this applies to all the techniques discussed hereafter) that a 2D spectrum is strictly a map of *connectivities* – through-bond or through-space – and that the chemical shifts of the original resonances are identified by inference from the map. A hypothetical nucleus with no connectivities to anything else would still be present, buried somewhere along the diagonal, but would not contribute to a crosspeak and so would effectively not be detectable.

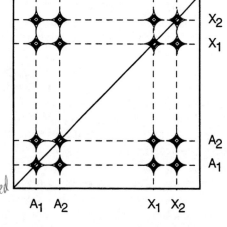

usually the diagonal is very complicated with lots of signals.

Sixteen-peak spectrum represented as a contour map.

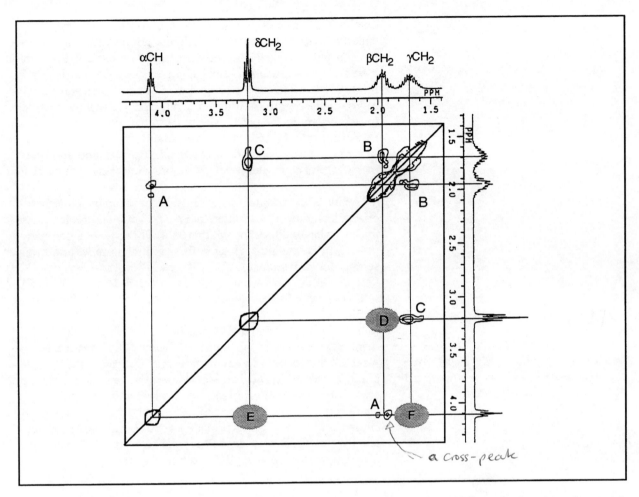

*A simple example of COSY – the spectrum of arginine. The exchangeable NH and COOH protons have been deuterated (solution is in D_2O), so the spin system is αCH-βCH_2-γCH_2-δCH_2. The COSY crosspeaks are **A** (connectivity between αCH and βCH_2), **B** (βCH_2 to γCH_2) and **C** (γCH_2 to δCH_2). In the lower half of the plot the markers **D**, **E**, and **F** show longer-range connectivities revealed by a TOCSY or HOHAHA experiment (see section 4.9).*

4.6 Notes on COSY

(a) The important thing revealed by the COSY spectrum is the *presence* of spin couplings. The exact size of the couplings is largely irrelevant – though if we can contrive to measure them, J-values can be of great value in structural analysis. In one dimension, J-values can only be measured accurately if the spectrum can be displayed at a very high resolution; only in this way can the identical J values of two coupled resonances be properly established. To display J-values to an accuracy of, say, 0.1 Hz in a normal one-dimensional spectrum is very difficult with all but the smallest molecules, and requires very careful setting up of the spectrometer. It also requires very high digital resolution: a 0.1 Hz resolution will require at least 30,000 data points to cover a 3 kHz spectrum width. In 2-D spectra, because the crosspeaks directly reveal the partners in spin couplings, the spectrum does not need to be nearly as well resolved. This has two important benefits. Firstly, data can be collected

	Pulse 1	Pulse 2	Receiver	Store as
1	x	x	x	Real
2	x	-x	x	Real
3	y	y	y	Real
4	y	-y	y	Real
5	-x	-x	-x	Real
6	-x	x	-x	Real
7	-y	-y	-y	Real
8	-y	y	-y	Real
9	y	x	y	Imaginary
10	y	-x	y	Imaginary
11	-x	y	-x	Imaginary
12	-x	-y	-x	Imaginary
13	-y	-x	-y	Imaginary
14	-y	x	-y	Imaginary
15	x	-y	x	Imaginary
16	x	y	x	Imaginary

Phase cycle of pulse 1, pulse 2, and receiver for phase-sensitive COSY experiment with quadrature detection.

quickly. Remember that to get a resolution of R Hz you need to collect data for $1/R$ seconds; if 5 Hz resolution will do, an FID need be collected for only 0.2 seconds. Secondly, the computer requirements don't become impossible. If you only want around 5 Hz resolution in a 3 kHz spectrum width, 512 points will suffice to represent the spectrum. Bearing in mind that we will need to collect the equivalent of 256 or 512 one-dimensional spectra to give us one two-dimensional COSY spectrum, perhaps this is just as well! Even so, even a 512x512-point dataset will take up over a quarter of a megaword of computer memory – more while it is being processed.

(b) Artifacts are introduced into the 2-D spectrum by a number of effects, including T_1 relaxation, noise, and various complex phase problems beyond the scope of this book. These are overcome in practice by *cycling* through a number of different pulse and receiver settings for each successive FID. The cycle for phase-sensitive COSY (left) uses sixteen successive different sets of pulse and receiver settings, so you have to collect FID's in multiples of 16 for each t_1.

(c) A major application of COSY in biological NMR is the assignment of resonances within the spin systems of the amino acid residues. Spin couplings are not transmitted through the peptide bond, so each amino acid amide, alpha-carbon and sidechain forms an isolated system of coupled spins. Each of these systems gives a characteristic pattern of crosspeaks once chemical shifts are included, and these patterns provide a good starting point for the lengthy process of resonance assignment for the whole protein. (See diagrams on this and the next two pages)

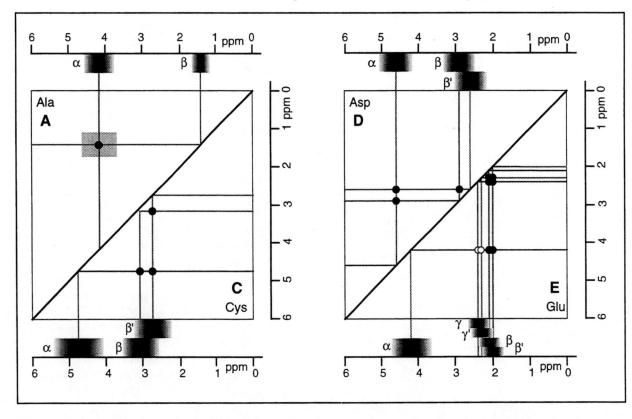

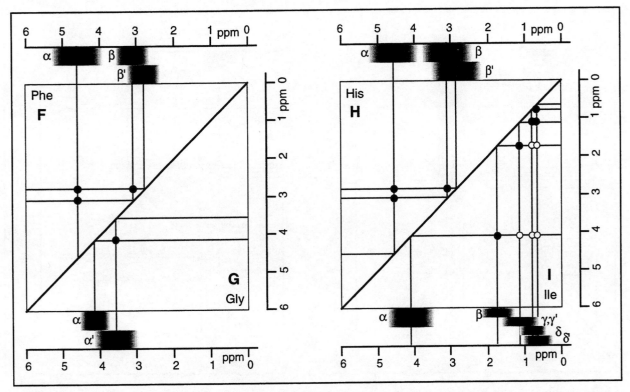

Diagrams on these and the next page are schematic representations of two-dimensional proton spectrum patterns for the twenty natural amino acids. Shaded bands indicate the chemical shift range for a particular proton: black circles indicate signals visible in a COSY spectrum, while open circles indicate additional signals seen using techniques such as TOCSY or HOHAHA as described in section 4.9. (Diagram continued overleaf.)

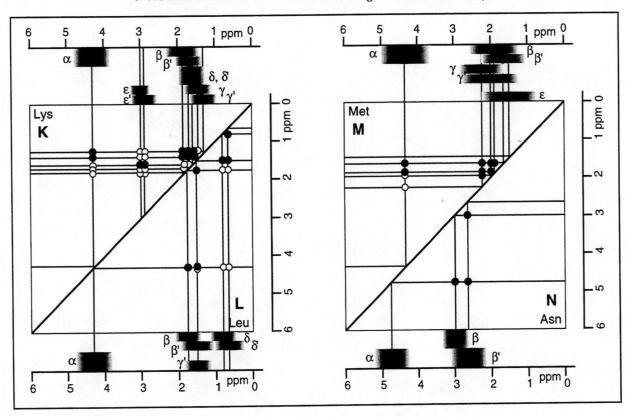

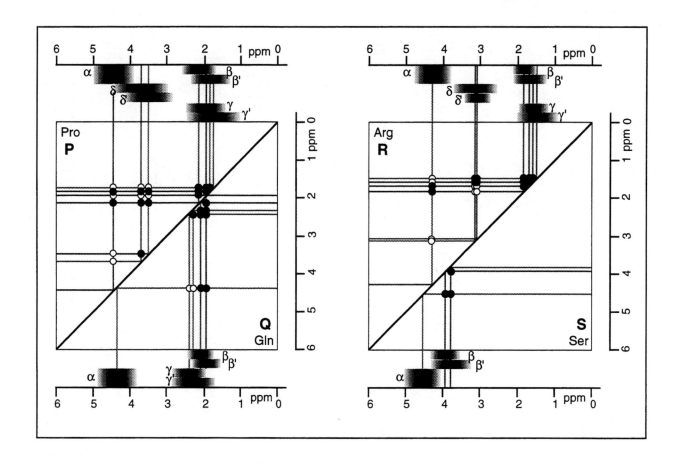

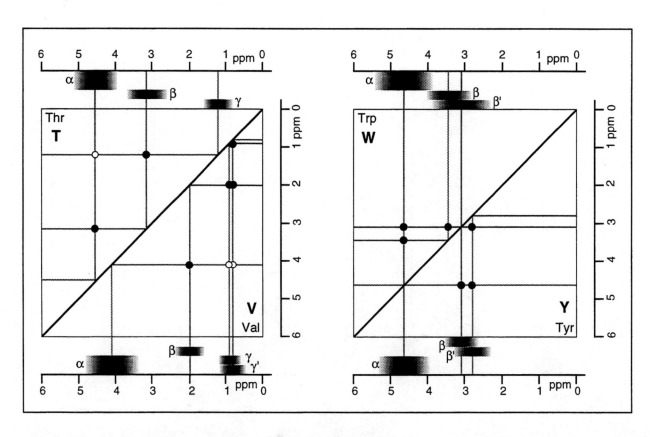

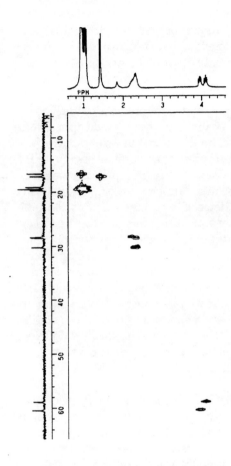

Part of the heteronuclear COSY spectrum of valinomycin: carbon-13 spectrum on left edge, proton spectrum above.

4.7 Simple heteronuclear shift correlations

Much important work depends on nuclei other than protons, and particularly carbon-13. Given both ^{1}H and ^{13}C spectra of the same compound, it is obviously of the greatest help to know which hydrogen atoms are attached to which carbon atoms. Since there is a spin coupling between ^{1}H and the ^{13}C to which it is covalently bonded, we can perform almost exactly the same experiment as before. Coherence which is generated on protons may be transferred to coupled ^{13}C nuclei as readily as to other protons: all that is required is a separate transmitter operating at the ^{13}C resonance frequency and a probe which permits irradiation and detection at both carbon and proton frequencies. There are now two separate sets of pulses:

$$\text{protons:} \qquad 90° - t_1 - 90°$$

$$\text{carbon:} \qquad 90° - \text{acquire} (t_2)$$

This time, coherence is transferred from proton to carbon by the second proton pulse. This coherence was at a particular proton frequency during t_1, and is thus labelled with that frequency. It is detected during t_2 at the frequency of the carbon bonded (and thus spin-coupled) to that proton. Thus the 2D spectrum has proton frequencies in the ν_1 direction and carbon frequencies in the ν_2 direction, with crosspeaks indicating which protons are bound to which carbons. (In displaying such spectra, it is common to arrange a 1-D spectrum along each axis so that the crosspeaks actually appear at the intersection of peaks in the proton and carbon 1-D spectra, as at left.) A technical problem which arises during such an experiment is that the multiplets arising from carbon-proton coupling can be very complex and can confuse the spectrum. Just blotting out the couplings by saturating the signals (as in spin-decoupling) will not help – the experiment only works because of the couplings! Couplings in the ν_2 direction can be eliminated by leaving a carefully computed delay, related to 1/J, between the final pulse and the acquisition. For couplings in the ν_1 direction, a combination of decoupling irradiation and composite pulses is needed. The figure shows a proton-carbon correlated spectrum for the cyclic peptide antibiotic valinomycin.

A problem with heteronuclear correlation spectroscopy is that even if the molecules are labelled to 100% isotopic purity with ^{13}C, the sensitivity of the detection of ^{13}C is a factor of 50 or so lower than that for protons (Box 2.1). Collecting sufficient data for a 2D heteronuclear correlation spectrum is very time consuming. Fortunately, methods exist for the correlation of ^{13}C or ^{15}N with ^{1}H in which both excitation and detection are performed on protons, with intermediate coherence transfer to carbon or nitrogen; these methods give the full sensitivity of proton spectroscopy, and are outlined in Chapter 5.

4.8 Variants on COSY

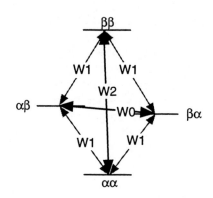

The "forbidden" transitions W0 and W2.

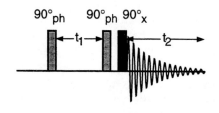

Pulse sequence for DQF-COSY. The pulses marked 90°$_{ph}$ are cycled through a sequence of phases to cancel out unwanted signals.

DQF-COSY. When two spins are coupled to each other, the energy level diagram of the two together is as shown at left. The transitions between states caused by a flip of *one* of the two spins are labelled W1, and it is these single-quantum transitions that are detected in NMR in the form of *single-quantum coherences*: rotating magnetisation at frequencies corresponding to the energies of transition between the levels shown. Other transitions would appear to be possible – the *zero-quantum* transition W0, in which spins are exchanged without the absorption or emission of energy, or the *double quantum* transition W2 in which both spins change states simultaneously. Such transitions are *forbidden* – that is, they do not produce a magnetisation detectable directly by an NMR experiment – and there is no way of picturing them in the classical formalism which we are using. However they do contribute to the mathematical terms of the quantum-mechanical description of the spin system, and thus can be made to contribute to the detected signal, even though they are not themselves detectable. In such experiments phase coherence may be transferred for a short time to a double quantum coherence before being returned to a single-quantum coherence for data acquisition. This is called double-quantum filtering, and the most useful related experiment is DQF-COSY.

A pulse sequence for DQF-COSY is shown at left. Its chief advantages over ordinary COSY are that only spins which are coupled to something else (i.e. are part of a double-quantum system) are present, totally eliminating most solvent peaks, and also that the resolution is improved, especially near the diagonal. Thus a DQF-COSY experiment makes it easier to measure J values for the analysis of spin-coupling.

Modifications of the DQF sequence can be used to produce triple-quantum filtering (TQF-COSY). In a TQF spectrum, only systems containing three mutually-coupled spins will appear; such systems are not found in proteins, but are common in carbohydrates.

When the highest resolution is required, for instance when J-values need to be calculated, several variants of COSY offer improved lineshapes and less overlap. These include E-COSY, PE-COSY, and PS-COSY.

4.9 Beyond COSY – RELAY, TOCSY, and HOHAHA

A COSY spectrum normally reveals the spin-coupling between neighbouring nuclei which are two or three bonds apart (H-C-C-H). Several methods exist for extending this analysis to give crosspeaks for other nuclei in a spin-coupled family – for example, all the

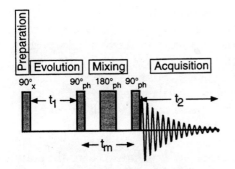

Pulse sequence for single-step relayed-COSY (RELAY) experiment.

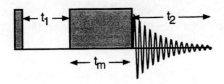

Sequence for TOCSY. The mixing time t_m can contain any of a wide variety of pulse sequences.

protons in a whole amino acid residue. Thus in a protein each amino-acid can be made to give a characteristic pattern of cross-peaks in the 2D spectrum, as shown in the diagrams on pages 56-58. This analysis is assisted by the fact that the peptide bond does not transmit couplings from one amino acid to the next along the protein chain, so that each amino acid remains as an isolated system of coupled spins.

All the methods depend on the insertion into the mixing time, between the end of evolution time t_1 and the start of data collection, of a series of pulses which irradiate the sample in various ways to transfer the phase coherence further through the coupled spin systems.

The first to be reported was *relayed COSY* (RELAY). In this, the mixing time is divided into two equal halves; 90° pulses are applied at the beginning and end of the mixing period, with a 180° pulse in between. The optimum length for the mixing time, given that the coupling constants between the nuclei are both equal to J, is 1/2J; if the coupling constants are not equal, a compromise mixing time is selected. The added pulses transfer magnetisation in two steps, producing crosspeaks between two resonances which are each coupled to a third, but not directly to each other. For example, where COSY would show crosspeaks between αCH and βCH, and between βCH and γCH protons of, say, lysine, RELAY would also show crosspeaks between αCH and γCH. The process can be repeated with additional pairs of 180° and 90° pulses, so that magnetisation is transferred sequentially through the spin system; however, efficiency falls off rapidly and longer-range connectivities are best achieved using HOHAHA or TOCSY sequences.

In the basic version of the *homonuclear Hartmann-Hahn* (HOHAHA) method a single coherent radiofrequency is applied during the whole of the mixing time, after a second 90° pulse. Since this is applied in the presence of rotating magnetisation M_{xy}, it acts as a *spin-lock*; the continuous irradiation effectively "drives" all the rotating magnetisations at its own frequency, overcoming the effects of chemical shift. In other words, the spins are forced to precess at the same frequency, as if they all had the same Larmor frequency. This satisfies the so-called *Hartmann-Hahn condition*; the spins are all precessing at the same frequency and experiencing the same strength of radiofrequency power. Under these conditions, magnetisation is transferred very efficiently, at a rate determined by J, between coupled nuclei. The longer the mixing time, the further through the spin system the magnetisation propagates. Thus coherence sharing can be controlled: magnetisation that is transferred from proton A to proton M during the first half of the mixing period will be relayed in part to proton X during the second half. Thus HOHAHA with a short mixing time can reveal nearest neighbours, just as COSY does, and as the mixing time is increased it can produce results like RELAY, finally giving a complete set of crosspeaks for the whole spin-coupled system like TOCSY.

In practice, HOHAHA spectra are produced not with a single spin-lock irradiation (which, because it is long, contains only a narrow band of frequencies and thus cannot irradiate the whole spectrum width efficiently), but with a rapid series of pulses with phases switched by 180°; an odd number of pulses (e.g. 49) may be repeated during the mixing time. A total mixing time of 50 ms may then reveal, for example, crosspeaks for NH with βCH, and NH with γCH, within single amino acids.

A way of producing a complete family of crosspeaks is the pulse sequence known as TOCSY (for TOtal Correlation SpectroscopY) which is essentially identical to HOHAHA. During the mixing time a sequence of 180° pulses with a fast repetition rate shares phase coherence throughout the entire system of coupled spins. At the end of the mixing time, the FID is collected as usual, but it now contains crosspeaks connecting every nucleus within the coupled system.

By combining COSY, RELAY, HOHAHA and TOCSY experiments appropriately, a gradually expanding number of crosspeaks appears, corresponding to the isolated spin systems which make up the molecule under investigation. The technical problems of setting up and operating these multiple pulse techniques are not trivial; they do, however, provide a way to build up a complete picture of the bonding patterns within a sample molecule.

4.10 The Nuclear Overhauser Effect and NOESY

All the effects we have discussed so far have been mediated by the electrons which link atoms together. The Nuclear Overhauser Effect (NOE) is different – it relies on interactions which occur across space, and can therefore provide information on nuclei which are adjacent in space but not linked through bonds. The effect is based on *cross-relaxation* – on transfer of magnetisation through *dipolar* coupling between nuclei (regarded as magnetic dipoles) rather than on *scalar* coupling through bonds. Overhauser effects are strongly distance dependent, falling off as the sixth power of the internuclear separation.

4.10.1 *The effect itself*

The nuclear Overhauser effect, which has been used for a long time in one-dimensional NMR, is the change in the *intensity* of one resonance when another resonance is perturbed (the perturbation employed is usually *saturation* – i.e. the populations of upper and lower energy states are equalised by continuous radiofrequency irradiation). If we observe the intensity I_0 of a resonance from

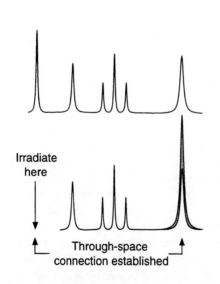

Irradiate
here

Through-space
connection established

The nuclear Overhauser effect: Irradiating at one resonance increases (or decreases) the intensity of signal from a nucleus which is within a few Ångstroms of the first.

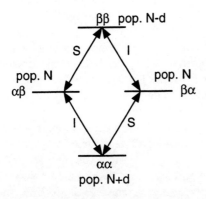

At equilibrium, the Boltzmann distribution ensures that the largest populations are in the lowest states.

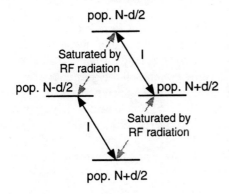

Irradiating the sample at the frequency of the S transition saturates it, equalising the populations at top and bottom of the transition. The population difference d remains across the I transition, so I signals are unchanged

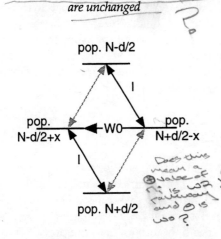

Zero-quantum (W0) relaxation across space decreases the population difference across I, decreasing the intensity of the I signal (negative enhancement).

nucleus i, then saturate some neighbouring nucleus s and find that the intensity I_0 has changed to I, the so-called *nuclear Overhauser enhancement* is:

$$n_{i(s)} = (I - I_0)/I_0$$

This is usually expressed as a percentage, and $n_{i(s)}$ can be positive or negative – the affected peak can get bigger or smaller.

Consider two nuclei I and S which are in the same molecule but NOT spin coupled to each other. Their energy level diagram is as shown in the diagram; the transitions of the two nuclei are a few ppm different in energy, but because they are not spin coupled both single-quantum transitions of each individual nucleus have exactly the same energy. The spectrum is just two single lines, one from each nucleus.

Now the Boltzmann distribution tells us that the lowest energy state has the largest population. For convenience we call this population N+d, the populations of the intermediate states N each, and the population of the highest state N-d (top diagram, this page). If we perturb the populations of any of the levels, the system will tend to relax back to this equilibrium distribution. The important thing to realise is that it may do this via *any* pathway W (see diagram at the top of page 60). In NMR we are only familiar with transitions such as W1 which involve a single-quantum jump, because they are the only ones directly detectable (See section 4.8 above). The other pathways, involving zero-quantum (W0) or double-quantum (W2) jumps, are classified "forbidden" because they are not spectroscopically detectable; they are, however, permitted to occur during the process of relaxation.

The basic one-dimensional NOE experiment proceeds as follows: with the system at equilibrium, we irradiate continuously at the frequency of the s transition so that it is *saturated* – that is, the populations at the top and bottom of the transition are equalised. The new populations are as shown (middle diagram, this page): we have transferred d/2 nuclei from the bottom to the top of each S transition. Note that this makes no difference to the signal from I: the population differences across the I transitions are still d, and thus the intensity of the I line is just as it was before, *unless relaxation takes place via the W0 or W2 pathway*. Such relaxation is only possible if the two nuclei are very close to each other in space – within 5 Å or so.

What happens next depends on whether W0 or W2 is the dominant pathway for relaxation:
(i) If W0 relaxation happens fastest, transferring spins from the N+d/2 to the N-d/2 level, it *increases* the population at the top of one I transition and *reduces* the population at the bottom of the other (bottom diagram, this page). The net result in both cases is that the intensity of the i line *decreases* (a negative NOE).

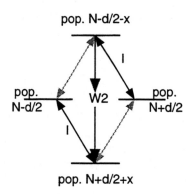

pop. N-d/2-x

I

pop.
N-d/2

W2

pop.
N+d/2

I

pop. N+d/2+x

Double-quantum (W2) relaxation across space increases the population difference across I, increasing the intensity of the I signal (positive enhancement).

(ii) Conversely, if W2 relaxation dominates, the intensity of the I line *increases* (a positive NOE).

Once the system has settled to dynamic equilibrium (still keeping the s transitions saturated with a constant radiofrequency irradiation) the value of $n_{i(s)}$ may be found: it is related to the relative rates of W0, W1 and W2, which in turn depend on the correlation time of the molecule and on the distance between the two nuclei. In practice positive NOE's are found for short correlation times (small molecules in non-viscous solution), and negative NOE's for long correlation times corresponding to large molecules or viscous solutions. A quantitative treatment shows that for a pair of spins i and s separated by distance r, and given the correlation time, the enhancement depends on the inverse sixth power of r, $(1/r^6)$.

4.10.2 Using the NOE in one dimension

The most common use for the NOE in this form is to compare internuclear distances between pairs of nuclei in two molecules which are similar and thus have essentially the same t_c and W values. Sensible results are only obtained if the sample is completely free of paramagnetic impurities, which perturb the relaxation – in particular this means the complete removal of all dissolved atmospheric oxygen from the solutions.

Normally NOE experiments as described are performed in one dimension and by using difference spectroscopy – a number of FID's is collected with the saturating irradiation on the s resonance, followed by a similar number with it turned off, and the difference between the two sets taken. (Note: in practice the saturating irradiation is not actually turned off, but only shifted away from the s frequency. This is because steady irradiation has a side-effect; it causes frequency shifts in all the resonances of the spectrum – the *Bloch-Siegert shift*. If all the resonances shift, you cannot do difference spectroscopy. However, leaving the irradiation switched on all the time, and just shifting it away from the spectrum, means that the effect will be the same for both sets of spectra, and the subtraction can be performed). Ideally, the difference spectrum will then contain only the resonance which is cross-relaxing with S.

4.10.3 Transient NOE's

Except in straightforward comparison and difference-spectroscopy cases, the interpretation of NOE experiments is fraught with problems, especially when more than two spins are involved. The presence of an NOE does not always prove beyond doubt that two protons are close together, and its absence does not prove that they are far apart. Helpful additional information can, however, be obtained by measuring the RATE at which the enhancement arises. For a given correlation time t_c this depends only on the distance between the nuclei. The saturation condition of the s nuclei cannot be achieved instantaneously, so instead it is found convenient to apply a selective 180° pulse to the s nuclei, wait a time t_m (the *mixing time*) and then apply the usual 90° detection pulse. A curve of the NOE against t_m has an initial slope which depends on internuclear distance.

4.10.4 Into the second dimension – NOESY and exchange

In our consideration of COSY (section 4.4) no use was made of the y' component of M_{xy} which was returned to the z' axis by the second 90° pulse. However, assuming that some molecular process was going on that would affect these spins, it might be of value to wait some time after the second pulse and then apply a *third* pulse that would tip this component back into the xy plane to see what had happened to it. This pulse sequence is the NOESY sequence:

$$90° - t_1 - 90° - t_m - 90° - t_2$$

Suppose that the phase coherence of a group of spins which was precessing with one frequency during t_1 were to migrate by cross-relaxation to another, nearby, site during t_m. It would then have a different frequency during t_2, and would produce a crosspeak in a two-dimensional plot revealing the chemical shifts of the two sites. Hence if there is an NOE between two sets of spins, this should show up as a crosspeak following the above pulse sequence. An exactly similar crosspeak would result if the transfer from one site to the other took place by chemical exchange. Thus a NOESY two-dimensional spectrum should have cross peaks due both to Over-hauser effects and chemical exchange. In many cases chemical exchange can be discounted because we are not looking at ex-changeable species, so any crosspeaks must reveal close proximity across space via the NOE. Because the perturbation of the s nuclei is by a pulse rather than a prolonged irradiation, this experiment is the 2D equivalent of the transient NOE described above.

The power of the NOESY experiment is in the very strong distance dependence of the cross-relaxation. Strong NOE crosspeaks will only be seen for nuclei less than about 2.5 Å apart, and weak ones for 2.5-3.5 Å. Extending the mixing time will permit nuclei sepa-rated by up to 5Å to produce crosspeaks, though not all such pairs of nuclei will produce anything detectable . Indeed, the absence of a crosspeak in a NOESY spectrum does not necessarily prove the absence of close approach, and a weaker crosspeak does not prove a larger internuclear distance; for this reason, NOESY peaks are often simply categorised as strong (1.8-2.5 Å), intermediate (1.8-3.5 Å), and weak (1.8-5.0 Å) with the same lower bound to the inter-nuclear distance.

Since 2D spectra are (or should be) symmetrical about the diagonal, it is now very common to show only half of the plot. It is then possible to show half of a COSY spectrum and half of a NOESY

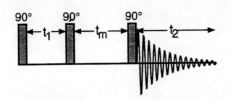

The basic NOESY pulse sequence.

what happens to the z element?

If chemical exchange produces similar results. How can you distinguish between the two.

spectrum in the same plot, and to use both in the assignment of resonances, which is an essential step in the determination of molecular structure using NMR.

4.10.5 ROESY

ROESY stands for Rotating-frame Overhauser Spectroscopy. In essence a ROESY experiment is the same as a HOHAHA experiment (see Section 4.9) in that a constant radiofrequency is applied to the sample for a mixing time which starts time t_1 after the original excitation pulse. This irradiation acts as a spin-lock, driving the rotating magnetisations in the sample at its own frequency rather than their individual Larmor frequencies. Under these conditions spin exchange is very efficient; this advantage is exploited in HOHAHA to spread coherence, labelled with the frequency of its originating nucleus during t_1, through a spin system. However, the

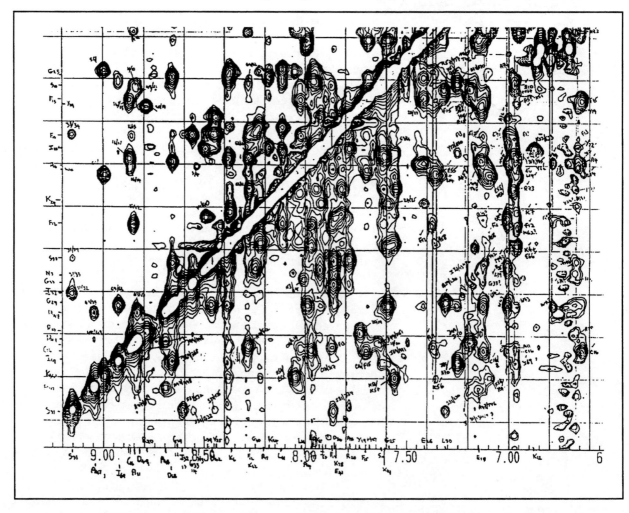

Part of the 600 MHz NOESY spectrum of HMG box 1, an 80-residue DNA-binding domain, with annotations from the assignment procedure (courtesy Drs. P.D.Cary and C.Read, University of Portsmouth). Section 5.7 gives a case study of the structure determination of HMG box 1.

efficient exchange of spins can also occur across space via the Overhauser effect: in order to reveal the resultant correlations independently of the stronger through-bond transfers, the irradiation in a ROESY experiment is less powerful than that used for HOHAHA, and its frequency is placed at one end of the spectral range rather than in the middle. These conditions do not satisfy the Hartmann-Hahn condition, so that only Overhauser crosspeaks are observed (though it pays to check!). ROESY is often used as a more efficient form of NOESY; it overcomes the tendency of NOESY peaks to disappear when molecular correlation times approach the Larmor frequencies being observed, a condition which afflicts molecules the size of smallish proteins.

4.11 The determination of small protein structures by homonuclear 2D NMR

4.11.1 Assignment of resonances and determination of contacts

By combining all the methods we have covered so far with the capacity to build computer models of protein structure with appropriate ϕ and φ angles and minimised energy, NMR can now be used to find the three-dimensional structure of a protein molecule. Homonuclear 2D spectroscopy is limited to proteins of molecular weight below about 10-12,000 daltons; the approach to larger molecules is covered in Chapter 5, but follows essentially the same strategy.

Before starting the process, we need to ask: How much data is needed, how much data is available? The answers to these questions decide the quality of the structure obtained. The progress of structure determinations has shown that the general fold of a protein backbone can be determined using, on average, about seven assigned NOE crosspeaks per residue. Each crosspeak represents a close approach between two nuclei, and so represents one *constraint* on the proposed molecular structure. Sidechains can be placed given about 10-12 constraints per residue, while a full structure determination needs from 15-20 constraints per residue upwards. It is fair to say that simple 2D homonuclear spectra can only reach this latter level in the best cases and for molecules below about 50-60 residues. Of course, these numbers of constraints are averages: you would expect the buried residues in the centre of a protein to have many detectable NOE contacts, while surface residues may have very few. Surface residues have fewer neighbours in any case, but more importantly their local motion and resulting reduced local correlation time t_c may reduce NOE intensities so that fewer crosspeaks are detectable. It follows that the conformations of protein cores will generally be better determined than those of surface residues.

Once the sample has been prepared and purified, and all the data has been collected, only the first stage (resolution) of the NMR study has been achieved (see section 3.10), and in many respects the work is just beginning. The assignment and interpretation of the data must follow, and the task should not be underestimated. A pile of large plots, each covered in unidentified spots, can be a daunting sight, and the strategy outlined below is not an automatic process. It demands considerable logic and patience, and no two studies can be relied upon to present the same difficulties.

The strategy is as follows:

(a) Assign proton resonances within amino acids. Starting from the COSY spectrum, and using chemical shift as a general guide, crosspeaks are assigned to amino acid types. As indicated by the diagrams on pages 56-58, some amino acid spin systems are unique: Gly, Ala, Thr, Ile, Val, Leu. On the other hand, all of Tyr, Phe, His, Trp, Cys, Asp, Asn, Ser are AMX systems (one αCH, and two βCH protons which are not usually equivalent, though they may be), and Arg, Lys and Pro are long spin systems. Of course, once a crosspeak is assigned to one residue type, it cannot be assigned again, so to an extent there is a built-in check. This first stage of assignment may be performed on a sample dissolved in D_2O, so that the αCH resonances are not split by amide NH protons and are more easily resolved; spectra in H_2O can then relate amide protons to their αCH.

The addition of data from RELAY, HOHAHA or TOCSY experiments will contribute additional crosspeaks, (see again pages 56-58) and should begin to provide redundant information that can be used to cross-check assignments already made. DQF-COSY or other higher-resolution methods may permit the observation of peak multiplets whose pattern may also help – for example, in D_2O solution where there are no backbone NH-αCH couplings, the αCH resonances from the amino acids with only one proton on their β-carbon (Thr, Ser, Val) will be doublets, those from most other residues triplets, and alanine αCH resonances will be quartets. In cases where there are stereospecific ambiguities, for example two nonequivalent β-CH protons, it may be possible to resolve the problem using J-values; otherwise it may prove necessary to represent both protons by a single 'pseudoatom' until a later stage in the structure determination.

(b) Assign resonances along the sequence. Once each crosspeak in the COSY spectrum has been assigned to an amino acid type, NOESY is used in the search for neighbouring residues. The commonest strong NOE crosspeaks in the spectrum will come from nearest neighbours along the sequence (diagram at left), and assuming the sequence to be known, there should be some unique dipeptide pairs which will give assignable crosspeaks. Once a particular pair has been identified, it should be possible to find the next one along, and so follow the sequence until a break occurs, perhaps at a proline residue which has no amide NH, or because there is an

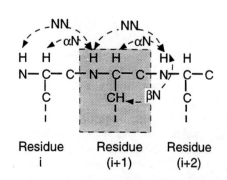

Some of the main along-chain proton NOE contacts for sequential assignment.

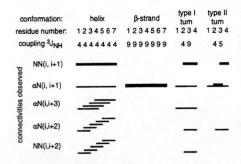

conformation:	helix	β-strand	type I turn	type II turn
residue number:	1 2 3 4 5 6 7	1 2 3 4 5 6 7	1 2 3 4	1 2 3 4
coupling $^3J_{NH}$	4 4 4 4 4 4 4	9 9 9 9 9 9 9	4 9	4 5

Expected NOE contacts for various secondary structures. The thickness of the lines indicates the expected strength of the NOE's; typical J values for NH-αCH couplings (in Hz) are also given.

ambiguity in assignment. The most important connectivities for sequential assignment are αCH(i)-NH(i+1), αCH(i)-NH(i+2), αCH(i)-NH(i+3), NH(i)-NH(i+1), βCH(i)-NH(i+1), and αCH(i)-βCH(i+1), some of which are indicated in the diagram (previous page).

(c) Assign secondary structure contacts. Once the direct nearest-neighbour NOE resonances have been assigned, there will be some unaccounted for. These will fall into two categories, the first of which will be produced by secondary-structure contacts. For example, an α-helix will always give contacts between residue i and residues (i+3) and (i+4), and other recognised secondary structures give characteristic patterns, as shown in the diagram at left which gives important contacts for common helical and β-structures.

(d) Analyse any J-coupling values that are available to give dihedral angles (or at least constraints on dihedral angles) using Karplus-type relationships (page 28). Large values of J tend to be the most useful, not least because small values are much more difficult to measure as their value approaches the average linewidth. Any accurate values that are available will allow the conformations of sidechains to be determined, though there is always a risk that rotation about bonds may be giving a dynamic average of J values from several different conformations. Even if only approximate J-values can be found, however, they will be helpful in the confirmation of secondary structure. For α-helices, $^3JNH-\alpha CH$ is around 4 Hz, while in the extended strands of β-structures it is in the range 8-10 Hz.

(e) Assign long-range contacts. NOE crosspeaks still unaccounted for will come from the vital long-range contacts – nuclei that are close in space, but distant along the protein sequence. These contacts provide the all-important distance constraints from which the tertiary fold of the protein will be deduced. They can be classified into *strong* (1.8-2.5 Å), *intermediate* (1.8-3.5 Å) and *weak* (1.8-5.0 Å) crosspeaks to help in specifying the bounds to be put on the structure.

As a result of the above efforts, there now exists a set of *constraints* – limits to specific distances and dihedral angles – to which the protein structure must conform. The more constraints there are, the more reliable will be the final structure.

4.11.2 Construction of a preliminary structure: – distance geometry

As well as the constraints identified from the NMR spectra, a protein structure is subject to many other geometrical restrictions: these are the so-called *holonomic* constraints, arising from the covalent structure of the molecule. This fixes within very close limits the interatomic distances between pairs of atoms which are bonded to each other and defines the steric hindrances which must not be violated; backbone dihedral angles must in general remain within the allowed regions of the Ramachandran plot, and of course the peptide bond must remain approximately planar. Any acceptable structure must naturally conform to these as well as the NMR constraints.

The problem of finding a model structure which fits the data and is unbiased – that is, not influenced by an experimenter's ideas – is approached using *distance-geometry* computer programmes. The purpose is to search for structures that are as consistent as possible with all the input data. Several approaches have been successful, and are very similar in the results they produce:

(a) The *metric-matrix distance-geometry approach*, exemplified by the program DISGEO, considers the distances between every pair of atoms in the structure. Each distance r_{ij} between any two atoms i and j becomes one element in a matrix. In some cases, for example where the atoms are directly bound to each other, this distance is known rather exactly. In others, say from NOE contact data, the distance has upper and lower bounds. Many other distances are of course completely unknown. Two matrices are constructed, one containing the *upper* limits to all the known distances, and the other containing their *lower* limits. A third matrix is then constructed in which each element corresponding to a bounded element in the other two is given a value which is randomly placed between the bounds. A computer algorithm (the *embedding algorithm*) is then used to construct three-dimensional structure corresponding to the interatomic distances of the third matrix. Randomly-determined but within all the known bounds, this is one possible structure for the molecule; it fits all the known data. The process is repeated for new sets of randomly-placed (within the bounds) distances; each time, a new structure results. These structures build into a family, each member different but each consistent with the data; the quality of the data is shown by how closely the family members resemble each other.

(b) The second successful approach is the *variable target function* method used, for example, by the program DISMAN. In this algorithm dihedral angles (rather than interatomic distances) are used as the variables, and these are varied to minimise deviations from the NOE distance constraints. At the beginning, the algorithm uses a small family of constraints local to a region of the molecule, gradually adding more long-range constraints as the early constraints are satisfied. Each refinement starts from a different initial structure with random dihedral angles, so that a family of structures are constructed, each successive model coming from a different starting point.

(c) As the database of known (from x-ray crystallography and NMR) protein structures increases in size, it becomes more likely that it contains substructures that are similar to parts of the protein being investigated. This provides the basis for methods of *knowledge-based* modelling. Local patterns of NOE constraints, say from 5-

Family of 30 backbone structures from preliminary studies of HMG box 1 (see Section 5.7).

10 residues of the molecule, can be compared with a database of similar constraints calculated from known protein structures. By "sliding" the experimental matrix along the database equivalents and scoring the similarities, regions of maximum fit can be identified and the corresponding database structures adopted for that region of the protein. Local structures so determined can be linked together through longer-range constraints.

4.11.3 Refining the structure, step 1: energy calculation

Once a family of structures has been calculated, it may be refined through the application of *molecular mechanics*. The distance constraints used so far do not take into account the energy of the folded structure; it is however a truism that the real molecular structure must represent a global energy minimum. It is not yet possible to calculate the true energy of folding of a protein, including entropic contributions from molecule and solvent, so if we want to do useful molecular energy calculations we have to resort to empirical formulations, taking into account the major contributions to the free energy of the molecule once it is close to its minimum energy. The actual figures obtained in this way for the energy will only be relative, but can still be minimised in the search for the "best" conformation of the molecule. We cannot use such methods to *predict* the three-dimensional structure of a molecule, but we can use them very successfully to *refine* the structure. The potential energy is calculated using the following terms:

(i) Covalent interactions:

•Bond lengths
A bond of equilibrium length b_o but distorted to length b and having force constant K_b will contribute

$$E_{\text{bond length}} = \tfrac{1}{2}K_b(b-b_o)^2$$

•Bond angles
A bond of equilibrium angle θ_o but distorted to angle θ and having force constant K_θ will contribute

$$E_{\text{bond angle}} = \tfrac{1}{2}K_\theta(\theta-\theta_o)^2$$

•Torsional angles (dihedral angles)
The energetics of torsion angles can be very complex: this complexity may be represented by a many-term series of which the first term only is often used:

$$E_{\text{torsion}} = \tfrac{1}{2}K_\phi(1+\cos(n\phi-\delta))$$

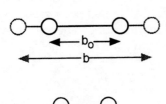

Parameters for energy calculations: top, bond length; middle, bond angle; bottom, torsion angle.

(In considering the energy contribution of each covalent interaction, we note that $K_b \approx 800 - 4000$ kJ mol^{-1}Å^{-2}, $K_\theta \approx 200 - 500$ kJ mol^{-1}rad^{-2} and $K_\phi \approx 5 - 25$ kJ mol^{-1}rad^{-1}. Thus bond lengths and bond angles are heavily constrained, while dihedral angles can vary much more readily with only a small energy penalty.)

(ii) Noncovalent interactions:

• Electrostatic interactions
These are represented by the Coulomb inverse-square law. Often atoms are assumed to carry a partial charge. A major problem is what assumptions to make about the nature and value of the *dielectric constant* within a molecule; that is, the effect on electrostatic forces of the medium between the interacting charges. One rule of thumb is to make the dielectric constant equal to the separation between the charges in Å: another is simply to assume it to be 1. There is clearly a need for more refined models of dielectric constant within molecules.

$$E_{electrostatic} = q_1 q_2 / Dr^2 \text{ where D is a constant}$$

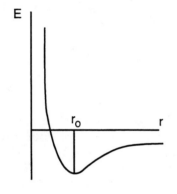

Form of the Lennard-Jones potential.

• van der Waals forces (dispersion forces)
These are the forces (always attractive) which exist between all atoms which are close together. They may be approximated by a mathematical expression incorporating a short-range attractive term and an even shorter-range repulsive term. A variety of approximations is available, one of the most commonly used being the *Lennard-Jones*, where A and B are constants:

$$E_{van der Waals} = A/r^{12} - B/r^6$$

• Hydrogen bonds
Hydrogen bonds make a considerable contribution to the energy of a folded protein molecule. 90% of all buried polar groups in a protein are involved in one or more hydrogen bonds The energy of a given bond depends on its length r and its geometry.

$$E_{hydrogen bond} = \frac{A'}{r^m} - \frac{B'}{r^p} \ f(\theta', \theta'')$$

where A', B' are constants, m and p are often 12 and 10 (but may be 6 and 4!), and f is a function of θ' and θ'', which are the angles to donor and acceptor atoms.

• NMR constraints
To this list of empirical molecular energy terms we add an extra, notional, term E_{nmr} that represents the distance constraints determined from NMR and exacts an energy penalty if these are exceeded. The "energy contribution" of these constraints may be made arbitrarily large to begin with, and then eased as the molecule settles towards a low-energy structure. Ideally, of course, "energy" contributions from this source should eventually reduce to zero; if correct, the final structure should naturally incorporate NMR distance constraints without any additional encouragement.

The process of energy calculation starts from the coordinate set which represents the preliminary structure for the molecule, based on the distance-geometry calculations. From this all the internal values for bond lengths, bond and dihedral angles, and interatomic distances are calculated. A value for the potential energy is then found using the above terms, and all the contributions are added together (Σ means "sum over all atom pairs")

$$\text{Total potential energy} = \Sigma E_{\text{bond length}} + \Sigma E_{\text{bond angle}} + \Sigma E_{\text{torsion}}$$

$$+ \Sigma E_{\text{electrostatic}} + \Sigma E_{\text{Lennard-Jones}} + \Sigma E_{\text{hydrogen bond}} + \Sigma E_{\text{nmr}}$$

Note from the earlier definitions of these terms how many of them are empirical. This is not of great importance for refinement of structures, provided that the quantities calculated are correct *relative* to one another. A number of computer packages are commonly available to perform such energy calculations, among them CHARMM, AMBER, and GROMOS. Each uses a slightly different approach and set of constants.

4.11.4 Refining the structure, step 2: energy minimisation

Once the energy of a given molecular conformation has been calculated, the conformation may be varied in a search for the lowest energy and hence, presumably, the best structure. The energy of, say, a single bond stretching can be represented on a simple graph with bond length as the x-axis and energy as the y-axis. The energy of *two* such bonds must be represented as an *energy surface* over a two-dimensional base. By extension of this argument, the energy depending on the variation of 3n parameters can be represented as a "surface" in 3n-dimensional space. (Note: 3n parameters, for example x, y and z co-ordinates, are needed to specify a molecule with n atoms. A protein with 300 atoms – say 30 amino acid residues – needs 900 parameters). Given a surface in many-dimensional space that represents the sum of the empirical energy terms of a particular protein structure it is then assumed that at some point on this surface will be a unique *global minimum* which represents the "best" structure for the molecule. If the surface everywhere sloped evenly towards this minimum we would have no problems finding the best structure; however, the surface is very uneven (it has been described as a multi-dimensional egg-box) with many *local* minima. Unless a search for the global minimum starts from a point already very close to the true minimum, it is going to end up in a local minimum which is probably very far from the global minimum we seek. Consequently energy minimisation techniques are restricted to the refinement of structures, such as the results of distance-geometry calculations, which are already known fairly accurately, or to the relaxation of strained structures. Searching the whole of the available conformation space to build an energy-minimised structure from scratch is at present an impossibly large task.

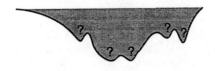

Local minima...

Given these limitations, energy minimisation algorithms may be categorised as follows:

Search methods employ one of a number of search patterns to look for a minimum in the energy surface, along one (univariate) or more (multivariate) axes at a time (remember there will be 3n axes for our 3n-dimensional space). The methods may be very slow since there are a lot of parameters to search. The SIMPLEX method described by Robson and Platt[†] allows the sampling of many minima not just by their energy but by a variety of global characteristics including hydrophobic packing and chain fold patterns.

Gradient methods such as that of *steepest descents* increment the structure parameters in steps *opposite to the gradient of the surface* at that point. An important feature of these methods is to calculate the optimum step length to give a reasonably efficient search. Gradient methods converge slowly to a minimum, but are useful for introducing small or local changes, such as removing bad contacts.

Newton-type methods use variants of the *Newton-Raphson algorithm* commonly used for equation-solving by successive approximation. As normally used, the algorithm cycles though the calculation:

$$x_{r+1} = x_r - F(x_r)/F'(x_r)$$

and successively substitutes x_{r+1} for x_r until the two become identical within some predetermined margin. In this equation, $F'(x_r)$ is the first derivative of $F(x_r)$; because we are looking for a minimum, we use gradients F' and second derivatives F'' instead of F and F'; also, because we are working in many dimensions the gradients and derivatives have to be expressed in *matrix* form – the matrix of second derivatives is called the *Hessian matrix*. Large numbers of matrix operations are very demanding of computer time, and a fast machine is needed to minimise energies in a reasonable amount of time.

4.11.5 *Refining the structure, step 3: molecular dynamics*

Models of proteins, built from metal or plastic or on a computer screen, are static. The mental picture formed by such models is misleading: molecules are in fact in a state of continuous, almost fluid motion as a result of thermal energies. This overall motion may be seen as the sum of a large range of components, having amplitudes of motion between 0.01 and 100 Å, energies from 0.1 to 100 kcal mole^{-1}, and frequencies between 10^{15} Hz and 10^{-3} Hz. Local motions involve single atoms, amino acid sidechains or loops of a few residues. Whole helices, domains or subunits may move as rigid bodies. Large-scale opening-closing, folding or unfolding of the protein occurs. And through all this there will be elastic and inelastic vibrational modes involving large numbers of coupled atoms. A brief discussion of the ways in which NMR can contribute to our knowledge of molecular dynamics will be found in Chapter

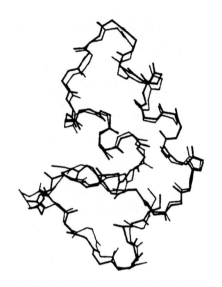

Crambin backbone (thick line) derived from simulated annealing, superimposed on X-ray structure (thin line). Stages in the annealing process are shown opposite.

† *Journal of Molecular Biology* 188, 259, (1986)

6. Because of all these motions, a fully-folded protein at room temperature still samples an enormous number of conformations; the family of structures which result from distance-geometry experiments may reflect these.

The simulation of molecular dynamics in the computer is based on the empirical energy calculations outlined above. It is assumed (reasonably, if the protein does not denature) that the parameters, while changing as the molecule moves, do not stray far from their equilibrium values. In the most commonly used approach the first derivative of the potential energy with respect to each atom position is calculated. This provides the force acting on the atom when it is displaced, and permits the solution of Newton's laws of motion for the atoms.

The process is then as follows: A model structure is first energy-minimised to relax local stresses. The atoms are then assigned velocities at random, the velocities corresponding to a Maxwellian distribution at some arbitrary low temperature. (The Maxwellian velocity distribution is that typical of the random motions of gas molecules at some absolute temperature T). The energy is calculated and recalculated over a period of a few picoseconds on the molecular time scale. This process is then repeated for Maxwell velocities corresponding to successively increasing temperatures. The molecular motions have settled to equilibrium when:
(i) the simulated molecule temperature (measured by putting the

Steps in the annealing of crambin over a simulated period of 30 picoseconds.
Crambin diagrams courtesy of Drs.G.M.Clore and A.Gronenborn: see FEBS Letters 239 129-136 (1988)

average kinetic energy $\frac{1}{2}mv^2=\frac{3}{2}kT$) does not change over a simulated period of 10 ps or more.

(ii) all regions of the molecule are at the same temperature.

(iii) the simulated atomic motions remain in a Maxwellian distribution.

By "heating" the molecule to a high temperature in this way, and then allowing it to "cool", the result of restrained molecular-dynamics calculations should be to remove the structure from any local energy minima, and thus increase the chances of finding the desired global minimum that best represents the real molecular structure. Such simulated annealing is commonly used as the final stage of a structure determination.

To simplify the molecular-dynamics calculations for large molecules, it may be possible to employ a *stochastic* approach in which the motion of only part of the molecule is calculated in detail, the rest of the molecule acting as a heat bath, that is a source of randomly-fluctuating forces on the region being investigated.

4.12 How good are NMR structures?

Clore and Gronenborn[‡] classify NMR structures into generations, giving the average atomic root-mean-square deviations (rmsd) of atom positions between the members of a family of structures which are all consistent with a particular data-set: this analysis makes a fourth-generation NMR structure the equivalent of an x-ray crystallographic structure with resolution in the region 2-2.5 Å. Several comparative studies using x-ray and NMR methods on the same molecule seem to bear this out: differences do occasionally appear, but can probably be explained by actual structural variations reflecting the difference between the solution and crystal environments, or to simple errors in one or other structure determination.

A powerful way of checking on the accuracy of a structure model from NMR is to use the model to calculate a predicted NOESY spectrum and to compare this with the data originally gathered. A good correlation between the two lends considerable credence to the model. It is possible to predict not only the positions of the peaks, but also their intensities, by using a "relaxation matrix" analysis. Differences between the experimental and calculated spectra can be used to calculate a *residual index*, similar to that calculated for x-ray structures, which is an indication of the reliability of the data. The relaxation matrix treatment also provides a further route by which data may be refined, since the relaxation matrix calculation may be reversed to improve the number and accuracy of distance constraints[†].

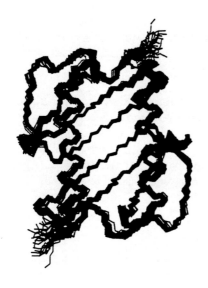

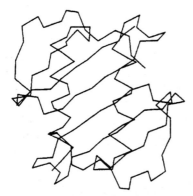

Comparison between NMR family (above) and X-ray crystallographic structures of interleukin-8. Diagram courtesy of Drs.G.M.Clore and A.Gronenborn; see J.Mol.Biol. 217 611-620 (1991).

Generation	Number of constraints per residue	rmsd (backbone)	rmsd (all atoms)
First	≈7	1.5Å	2.0Å
Second	≈10	0.9Å	1.2Å
Third	≈13	0.7Å	0.9Å
Fourth	≈16	0.4Å	0.5-0.9Å

‡Clore, G.M. and Gronenborn, A., *Science* 252 1390-1399 (1991)
†James, T.L., *Current Opinion in Structural Biology* 1, 1042-53 (1991)

Combining isotopic labelling with 3D spectra provides a powerful tool for larger molecules

5.1 Into the third dimension: homonuclear 3D

The improvement in resolution obtained by spreading the resonances of a one-dimensional spectrum into two dimensions has revolutionised NMR, making it possible to perform structural determinations on proteins of up to perhaps 70-80 residues – some say 100. At this point the limitation of resolution reasserts itself: the increasing number of resonances, coupled with greater linewidths, leads again to overlap which prevents proper analysis. In addition, as the increasing linewidths approach and then exceed the rather small three-bond J couplings between protons, the efficiency with which magnetisation is transferred rapidly falls, so that connectivities are less readily detected. In order to progress to larger molecules and more complex spectra, a further improvement in resolution is essential. Incremental improvements promised by spectrometers of higher frequency are slow in coming; fortunately we do not have to wait for them. The next step is conceptually simple for anyone who has understood thus far: it is an extension to another dimension.

In 2D NMR, we collected data as a function of two times, the evolution time t_1 which was systematically varied, and the acquisition (or detection) time t_2 during which the data was collected, and then performed two Fourier transforms on the resulting two-dimensional matrix of data points. The resulting spectrum, revealing through-bond or through-space connectivities, was then displayed in two dimensions. For three-dimensional NMR, the process is extended by making the original data dependent on *three* times, now systematically varying t_1 and t_2, and collecting data during t_3. The result is a three-dimensional matrix of data, which is processed using three transforms. To construct the experiment, we need only imagine a combination of two two-dimensional pulse sequences to give the required dependence on t_1, t_2 and t_3; the detection period of the first sequence, and the preparation period of

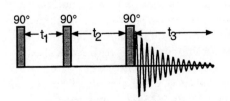

Sequence for 3-dimensional homonuclear COSY experiment.

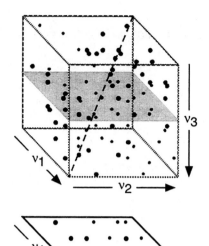

Top, a cube of data dependent on three frequencies ν_1, ν_2, ν_3. Bottom, a slice taken from the cube at a particular ν_3.

the second are omitted. Such a sequence, shown in the diagram, would give rise to a type of three-dimensional COSY spectrum which would be analogous to a RELAY experiment; coherence transferred through one bond by the first pulse would be transferred on (or back) by the second, giving rise to crosspeaks which were off the main body-diagonal of a cube representing the three frequencies ν_1, ν_2, and ν_3. Coherence which was not transferred at all would remain on the diagonal. Viewing a cube of data would be difficult, but of course there is no problem in slicing the cube to give a *stack* of 2D spectra, with fewer connectivities on each layer than would be found in the 2D spectrum.

Of course, collecting data for such a stack of spectra is going to take longer than collecting a 2D dataset; this is offset to some extent by the fact that the improved resolution requires less digital resolution so that fewer data points need be collected for each set of t_1, t_2 values. Perhaps 2-4 weeks would suffice to collect a complete 3D dataset using isotopic labelling (see below), depending on the sample and the technical difficulties experienced. This makes for quite expensive science: the running costs and capital depreciation of a high-field NMR spectrometer look very substantial when divided between only, say, ten or a dozen experiments a year.

While the improved resolution of a three-dimensional homonuclear COSY experiment is attractive, such experiments have found little favour in practice. The lineshapes of the detected signals often lead to cancellation of intensity, so that sensitivity is low. In addition, there are far more crosspeaks in homonuclear 3D spectra than in 2D, so the results are still hard to interpret. But probably the main reason why homonuclear 3D experiments are rarely used is the vastly greater power of three-dimensional *heteronuclear* experiments using isotopically labelled samples, particularly with ^{13}C and ^{15}N labels.

5.2 Isotopic labelling

Ever since the first one-dimensional spectroscopy of macromolecules revealed the problem of peak overlap, ways have been sought to simplify spectra. An obvious approach was to remove the majority of the detectable resonances by selectively substituting NMR-passive nuclei (i.e. nuclei of isotopes which do not have a magnetic moment, or of isotopes whose resonance is remote from those being observed) in the sample in the place of NMR-active isotopes of the same elements; this constitutes *negative labelling* because it simplifies the spectrum by removing a large number of resonances from it. Alternatively it is possible to substitute, at selected sites, NMR-active nuclei for NMR-passive ones (*positive labelling*). Thus, for example, negative labelling might replace the majority of hydrogen atoms in a sample by deuterium atoms to simplify the proton spectrum, and positive labelling might replace ^{12}C nuclei by ^{13}C at a few selected sites to produce a simple (and hence readily assigned) ^{13}C spectrum.

These early experiments, pioneered by Crespi and Katz in the '60's and early 70's, proved very difficult in practice. It is certainly possible to grow algae in deuterium oxide, and with carbon dioxide as the only carbon source and ammonium salts as the only nitrogen source: amino acids labelled with deuterium, or with chosen nitrogen or carbon isotopes, can then be isolated and separated for use in nutrient media for bacteria. In theory, this approach could be used either to label all amino acids in a protein, or, by adding only certain labelled amino acids to an otherwise unlabelled mix, amino-acid-specific labelling. However, the metabolic pathways of bacteria often prevent carefully-prepared labels from being incorporated in the anticipated manner; in addition, yields of material from both algae and bacteria were unimpressive and the whole process proved very expensive. Consequently isotopic labelling experiments, whether specific or general, were rather rare for perhaps fifteen years after they were first shown to be possible.

All this changed with the development of recombinant DNA methods and the consequent ability to over-express proteins in suitably engineered bacterial strains. This simultaneously brings two benefits: properly controlled overexpression can give high yields of the desired protein, and both native and site-specifically mutated eukaryotic proteins can be expressed in prokaryotic systems. However, labelling with specific amino-acids still remains a problem because of the 'scrambling' of labels by the metabolic pathways of the bacteria; labelling with aromatic amino acids is straightforward because their presence turns off biosynthesis in the bacterium, but specific labelling with other amino acids can be more difficult.

Fortunately, the need for specific or site-directed labelling is now much less than it was. The reason is the extension of NMR methods to two and three dimensions, and the development of proton-detected heteronucleus-edited spectra (see section 5.3). Using such methods, the need for specific site-directed labelling is removed: uniform labelling, replacing *all* the nitrogen-14 atoms in the molecule with ^{15}N, or all the carbon-12 atoms with ^{13}C, is the requirement for this kind of spectroscopy. Such labelling can be achieved, using *E. coli* for example, by growing the bacteria on minimal medium containing ^{15}N ammonium salts as the only nitrogen source, or ^{13}C glucose as the only carbon source. No laborious preliminary preparation of labelled amino acids using algae is necessary, the precursors are relatively affordable, and the labelling is carried out at a reasonably high efficiency. Of the two labels, ^{15}N can be incorporated about ten times more cheaply than ^{13}C at the time of writing; labelling an NMR-sized sample currently (1994) costs a few hundred pounds for ^{15}N and perhaps a thousand for ^{13}C, given a good expression system.

The protocol usually adopted uses a so-called *inducible promoter*, so that the protein of interest is not synthesised until conditions are optimal in terms of cell density and growth rate. Following induction, the majority of protein produced by a good expression system is the protein of interest. If specific (specific to particular amino acid types) labelling is still required, an expression system with an inducible promoter has the advantage that synthesis of the required protein runs ahead of amino acid biosynthesis: if a labelled precursor amino acid is introduced as expression is induced, the great majority of the amino acids incorporated in the expressed protein are labelled ones from the medium, and not freshly synthesised ones with no labelling.

5.3 Multiple quantum coherences

As long as the carbon atoms in a sample are ^{12}C, and the nitrogen ^{14}N, the only connectivities revealed by COSY and HOHAHA are based on two- or three-bond scalar couplings between protons, and only proton chemical shifts are resolved in the 2D or 3D spectrum. The ^{12}C nuclei have spin quantum number zero and hence no resonance properties, simply providing the covalent bonds through which spin coupling is transmitted, and although the ^{14}N nucleus has a spin quantum number of 1 and therefore is NMR active, it also possesses an electric quadrupole moment which dominates its relaxation behaviour and prevents its use for most normal structure work with biological macromolecules.

However, as soon as ^{13}C or ^{15}N are introduced into the protein, the situation changes completely. These isotopes are spin $-^1/_2$ and NMR-active, and it is perfectly possible to transfer phase coherence between protons, ^{15}N and ^{13}C nuclei in any order by using appropriate pulse sequences. We have already touched on this possibility in section 4.6 where a pulse sequence is shown for heteronuclear COSY spectra. Simple heteronuclear spectroscopy of that kind has found its main application for smaller molecules, largely because the small magnetogyric ratios of ^{13}C and ^{15}N lead to low sensitivity of detection (see Box 2.1). However, it has its attractions. We can

The heteronuclear coupling constants J (in Hz) between the nuclei of a peptide backbone.

use one-bond connectivities, which are strong. The coupling constants between protons and nitrogen and carbon are large (see diagram). Finally, the chemical shift range covered by a carbon or nitrogen spectrum is much larger than that for protons, so the potential resolution is higher.

Given this appeal, it is clearly desirable to overcome the sensitivity problem if at all possible. The solution is to be found in a group of experiments most of which can be classified as *heteronuclear multiple-quantum resonance experiments with proton detection* (abbreviated to HMQC). These entail the generation of multiple quantum coherences – coherences corresponding to the "forbidden" zero-quantum and two-quantum (and higher) transitions which are not directly detectable, but which may nevertheless contribute to the evolution of spin systems during the experiment. The mathematical treatment of these coherences, which is essential to the design of pulse sequences and is the only fully satisfactory description, is beyond the scope of this book; fortunately the results of the experiments are readily understandable without the mathematical treatment. The essence is this: *phase coherence which is generated on protons is transferred to carbon or nitrogen for an evolution time and then transferred back to protons.* In such experiments, the overall sensitivity depends on the product $\gamma_e \cdot \gamma_d^{3/2}$ where γ_e is the magnetogyric ratio of the excited nucleus and γ_d is that for the detected nucleus. Thus if both excitation and detection are carried out on protons, full proton sensitivity is maintained, even though the magnetisation is temporarily transferred to another nucleus such as carbon or nitrogen during the experiment. We thus frequency-label the signals with carbon or nitrogen chemical shifts, while maintaining the full sensitivity of a protons-only experiment. Such experiments can be carried out in two dimensions to give high-sensitivity heteronuclear equivalents of COSY, HOHAHA and NOESY experiments: the figure shows a pulse sequence used to produce a 2D carbon-hydrogen correlation spectrum. In practice, such two-dimensional spectra are rarely used because the technique is so readily extended into three and even four dimensions.

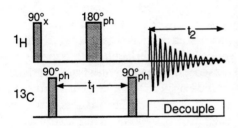

Pulse sequence for a 2D carbon-hydrogen correlation spectrum with proton detection.

5.4 3D heteronuclear techniques

(a) Molecules singly labelled with ^{15}N. Given a sample of perhaps 1 to 2 mM concentration of a protein uniformly labelled with ^{15}N, preliminary sequential resonance assignments are greatly assisted by ^{15}N-edited NOESY experiments, otherwise known as *NOESY-HMQC* (there is a ROESY equivalent – see Section 4.10). The pulse sequence used for such an experiment is as shown overleaf. The experiment starts with the excitation of all protons in the sample in the usual way, and after a frequency-labelling time t_1 a second proton pulse is followed by a mixing time as in a normal 2-dimensional NOESY experiment. During the mixing time magnetisation is transferred via the Overhauser effect between protons which are

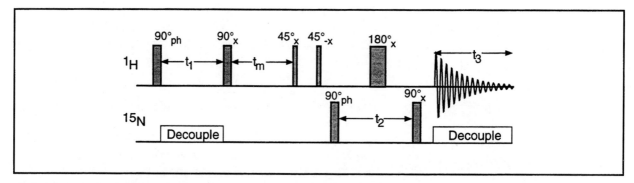

Pulse sequence for NOESY-HMQC spectroscopy of a ^{15}N-labelled molecule. The first part of the proton sequence is like a standard NOESY sequence, with frequency labelling during time t_1 followed by a mixing time t_m: it ends with a jump-and-return pair of $45°$ pulses to minimise solvent signal. Coherence is then transferred to the nitrogen nucleus, where it is frequency labelled during time t_2 before being transferred back to protons for detection during time t_3. To avoid splitting of the proton signals, spin coupling between nitrogen and protons is suppressed by a decoupling signal at the nitrogen frequency during t_1 and t_3.

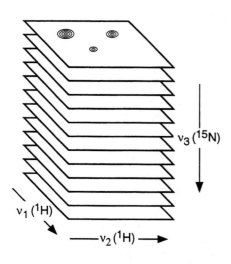

3D stack of spectra from the experiment above. Each slice shows connectivities involving protons bound to ^{15}N atoms at a particular (nitrogen) chemical shift.

close neighbours in space. A jump-and-return pulse pair is included to suppress solvent water resonances. Then a nitrogen-frequency pulse transfers magnetisation to nitrogen; after a second labelling time t_2, during which the magnetisation is labelled with the chemical shifts of the ^{15}N nuclei, a second nitrogen pulse transfers the magnetisation back to the amide protons – that is, *only to those protons which are directly bonded to ^{15}N atoms.* The magnetisation on these protons is then collected during period t_3. Thus the data collected is at the chemical shifts of the amide protons, but it is labelled with the frequencies of those protons which are close enough to them to exchange magnetisation *and also* with the chemical shifts of their attached nitrogen atoms. Three Fourier transforms will then give a stack of 2D NOESY spectra showing the neighbours of the amide protons, but with each layer of the stack distinguished by a particular ^{15}N chemical shift. Because these spectra reveal the protons closest to the amide groups, they are particularly valuable in sequential assignments, though of course they are not precluded from providing some of the precious long-range distance constraints as well.

Equally valuable in the assignment of resonances is the analogous ^{15}N-edited HOHAHA experiment, in which the abundant data of a HOHAHA experiment is spread over a number of planes defined by ^{15}N chemical shifts. The correlation this time, of course, is that between amide protons and their neighbouring α- and sidechain protons. Given a ^{15}N labelled molecule, another technique also appears for the determination of J values: ^1H-^{15}N HMQCJ.

(b) Molecules labelled with ^{13}C only. The chemical shifts of α-carbon proton, α-carbon itself, and carbonyl carbon nucleus form the three dimensions of the HCACO experiment. Magnetisation generated on protons is transferred to directly-coupled carbon atoms. After labelling time t_1, simultaneous α-carbon and carbonyl-carbon $90°$ pulses transfer the magnetisation to the carbonyl carbons. Note that these pulses can be selective for the appropriate regions of the

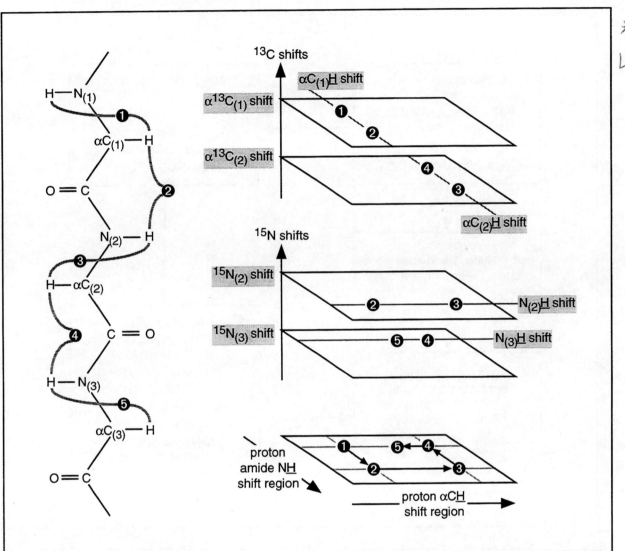

Combining two 3D experiments – carbon- and nitrogen-edited NOESY – to assign backbone proton signals sequentially along the chain. The protein is labelled with both 13C and 15N (or two samples may each be labelled separately). Proton-proton NOESY connectivities ❶,❷,❸,❹,❺ (above, left) can be made to appear in either 13C- or 15N-edited 3D experiments. In slices from a 13C experiment (top right), connectivities ❶ and ❷ appear on the same slice and at the same αCH proton shift because they both involve carbon C(1) and proton αC(1)H. Connectivity ❷ also appears on the 15N slice (middle right) corresponding to the nitrogen-15 shift of N(2), but is associated with connectivity ❸ because they both involve the N(2)H group. Thus by associating connectivities in pairs, assignments may be made along the backbone of the protein (bottom right).

carbon spectrum because of the very wide spread of carbon chemical shifts. Time t_2 then elapses to allow frequency labelling at the carbonyl frequencies, and the magnetisation is then transferred back in two stages to the α-carbon protons to permit detection during time t_3. The experiment does not involve amide protons, and can be performed in D_2O solution; if the sample is also labelled with 15N, this has to be decoupled during t_2.

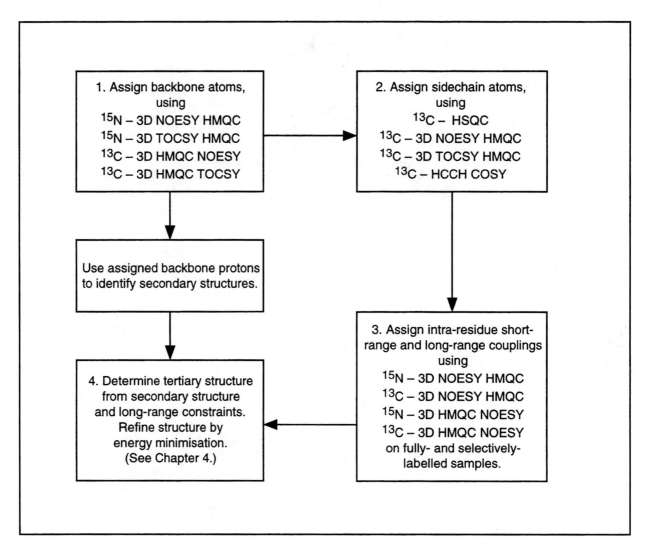

One possible flow diagram for protein structure determination using 3D heteronuclear techniques.

There are also, as might be expected, ^{13}C-edited equivalents of the ^{15}N-edited NOESY experiment described above, as well as HCCH-COSY and HCCH-TOCSY experiments

(c) Molecules labelled with both ^{13}C and ^{15}N. A variety of experiments is possible with doubly-labelled protein molecules, covering magnetisation transfer between all possible combinations of spin-coupled nuclei: HNCA, HNCO, HN(CO)CA, HCA(CO)N, and H(CA)NH (diagram opposite). All of these contribute to the assignment of resonances to their precise chemical shifts before the all-important NOESY distance constraints can be determined. In each case the principle is the same, but the design of the pulse sequence determines the pathway of the coherence before it is returned to protons for detection. The design and optimisation of pulse sequences for these experiments is extremely complex.

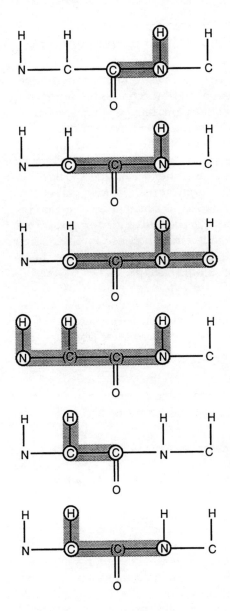

The main 3D experiments for backbones of double-labelled protein molecules: from top to bottom, HNCO, HN(CO)CA, HNCA, HA(CA)NHN, HCACO, HCA(CO)N.

(d) Analysis of ligand binding. A promising new application of isotope-editing is in the study of ligand binding to large molecules. The principle is quite straightforward: if a small molecule is labelled with ^{15}N or ^{13}C or both and then allowed to bind to a non-enriched receptor molecule, any isotope-edited spectroscopic method will reveal only signals from the ligand molecule. Thus a full structural determination of substrates, inhibitors or cofactors can be undertaken with the molecules in their bound conformation. For a short review the reader is referred to B.J.Stockman and J.L.Markley[†].

5.5 The fourth dimension

All the ideas we have discussed so far can be extended directly: the addition of a third systematically-varied evolution time to the pulse programme permits the labelling of the data with a total of *four* chemical shifts. These could be, for example, the shifts respectively of the originating proton, two separate intermediate carbon atoms, and the target proton. There is no point at all in trying to visualise a four-dimensional hypercube of spectral data, but of course the slice metaphor continues to serve: if 3D spectroscopy effectively turns a 2D spectrum into a stack of 2D spectra, 4D simply turns each member of that stack into a stack itself. The analogy in which a 1D spectrum is likened to one line of text, 2D to a page, and 3D to a book, is extended so that we now have a stack of books – an encyclopaedia of data. Because the data is now so spread out, the point-by-point resolution can be low, and collecting data for a 4D spectrum need not take much longer than for 3D – perhaps twice as long, but not much more. Three to eight weeks might be reasonable. In a four dimensional spectrum, of course, we are not concerned to measure linewidth, splitting, peak area or multiplicity: each resonance is simply a detected connectivity associated with the chemical shifts of four nuclei in the sample. Looking at the spectrum visually serves only to establish the presence of the signals, and what really matters is the unique set of four numbers associated with each one. It is the relationships between these numbers which make it possible to assign the resonances, and in four dimensions it should be possible to do that uniquely.

Particularly useful for the detection of long-range through-space contacts are 4D ^{13}C-^{13}C-edited and 4D ^{15}N-^{13}C edited NOESY spectra. The coherence is transferred successively via spin couplings with one NOE step, as follows:

originating ^{1}**H** → ^{13}**C** → ^{1}**H** ⟹ ^{15}N^{1}H → ^{15}**N**^{1}H → ^{15}N^1**H** *detected*

where the first two steps and the last two are via J-couplings, while the middle step (^{1}**H** to amide proton ^{15}N^1**H**) is a NOE connectivity. The double heteronuclear transfers in ^{15}N-^{13}C editing are very effective at removing artifacts from the spectrum: the equivalent ^{13}C-^{13}C experiment is much more difficult to optimise.

†*Current Opinion in Structural Biology* 2 52-56 (1992).

5.6 Computer-aided analysis of protein spectra

A number of programs have been devised for the automated or semi-automated assignment of NMR spectra. As resolution improves, with two, three, and then four separate chemical shift values being associated with each detected connectivity, the problems of simply keeping track of the data become enormous as a steady stream of assignments are made, frequently backtracking as later assignments prove an earlier educated guess to have been wrong. Available programs mostly provide good bookkeeping, and adopt the same stepwise approach as a manual analysis; for this reason they need to be manually checked as they progress. Recent developments begin to provide a more holistic approach, assigning resonances and analysing secondary structure at the same time: such are the MCD (main-chain-directed) packages.

A number of workers have settled on three dimensional homonuclear spectroscopy as the method of choice for automated assignment, rather than relying on heteronuclear labelling.

5.7 Protein structure with 3D: a case study

The example that follows describes structure determination of an 81-residue protein domain. The experiments were performed on unlabelled and fully ^{15}N labelled molecules: ^{13}C labelling was not used, at least partly because of the cost of ^{13}C precursors.

The HMG box is the name given to a family of similar protein domains which bind to bent, distorted or cruciform DNA. They are found in single or multiple copies as part of a number of very important regulatory proteins, including the male sex-determining SRY gene product and a number of enhancer-binding factors, as well as in the non-histone high-mobility-group chromosomal proteins from which they take their name. The HMG box has a minimum length of 71 amino acid residues, and maintains a stable tertiary structure in solution at high concentrations, making it a good candidate for NMR study. The following is an outline of the processes through which the structure was determined.

5.7.1 Preparation and purification of labelled protein.

The DNA sequence of HMG1 box 2 was amplified using the polymerase chain reaction from cDNA of chinese hamster. The amplified DNA was ligated into a vector plasmid in such a way as to code for a fusion protein, the HMG box being fused with glutathione S-transferase. Transformed *E.coli* cells were allowed to grow for three hours after inoculation of fresh broth, and then expression of the fusion protein was induced by the addition of IPTG. After three hours further growth, cells were spun down, resuspended and lysed. Cell debris was spun down and the supernatant was added to glutathione-complexed agarose beads. The glutathione S-transferase end of the fusion protein bound to these, and after thorough washing to remove all other proteins the HMG box was cleaved away from the fusion protein by digestion with thrombin and then purified by ion-exchange and gel exclusion chromatography. Ten litres of culture yielded about 50 milligrams of purified protein. For ^{15}N labelling the procedure was similar, but the only source of nitrogen in the growth medium was ^{15}NH$_4$Cl and the yield of protein was approximately halved: 25 mg from 10 litres of culture was just enough for one NMR sample. The purity and homogeneity of the protein were then confirmed by gel electrophoresis, mass spectrometry and partial sequencing, while sedimentation equilibrium experiments in an ultracentrifuge confirmed that the molecule was present in solution as a monomer.

5.7.2 Preliminary NMR studies

Exploratory 1D NMR at 270 MHz indicated that the sample began to denature at pH below 5 and temperatures above 30°C. All subsequent studies were performed at 24°C and pH 5.46, and on samples of concentration 4.8 mM – for these molecules, of molecular mass 9000 daltons, this corresponds to 43 mg/ml.

The main 2D and 3D spectra were recorded at 500 and 600 MHz. NH exchange was observed via nitrogen-proton heteronuclear single-quantum 2D experiments after dissolving a protonated sample in cold D$_2$O. NH-αCH coupling constants were obtained from a heteronuclear 2D HMQCJ experiment.

5.7.3 Assignments

Sequential assignment of amino acid spin systems was made by comparison of strips from the amide region of the 3D NOESY-HMQC spectra (left) and 3D HOHAHA-HMQC spectra. Stretches of spin systems connected by ^{15}NH-^{15}NH nuclear Overhauser effects were identified, with reference particularly to the amides for which spin system information was already clear (mostly glycine, alanine and aromatic residues). Breaks due to proline residues were bridged by using δCH-^{15}NH and αCH-^{15}NH connectivities, which were also used to resolve problems arising from overlapping NOE's. Sidechain assignments were obtained using 2D HOHAHA spectra of unlabelled samples in H$_2$O and D$_2$O. In the end, complete spin-system identification was achieved for 66 residues, along with a complete sequential assignment of backbone protons.

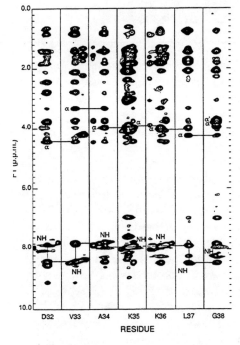

Amide strips for residues 32-38 of the HMG domain. Each strip may come from a different slice of the ^{15}N shift dimension: every connectivity shown must come from two protons within 5Å of each other, one of them being an amide proton. Inter-residue NH-NH connectivities are shown as NH, and NH-αCH connectivities as α.

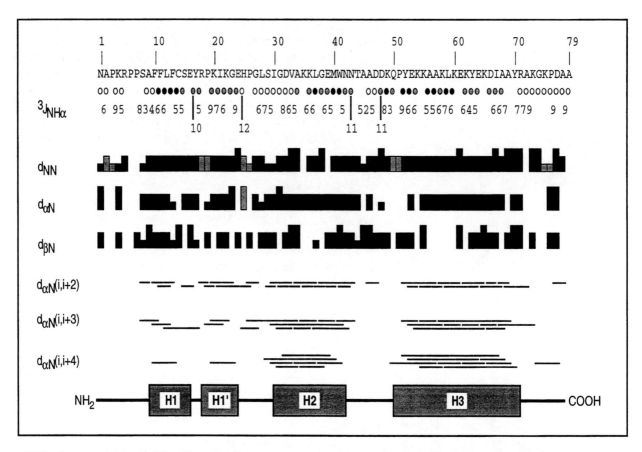

Table of connectivities for HMG box. Top line, sequence; second line, indication of exchange rates of amide protons; next line, NH-αCH coupling constants. NH-NH, αCH-NH, and βCH-NH connectivities are indicated as strong, intermediate or weak by line thickness. Intermediate-range couplings indicate the presence of four helices (bottom). (Diagrams on pages 87-89 are reproduced by kind permission of Dr.C.Read and Dr.P.D.Cary.)

5.7.4 Secondary structures

The key indicators of α-helical structure are αN(i+3) and αN(i+4) NOE contacts (see diagram, page 69). As indicated in the diagram above, these were apparent for residues 10-16, 19-24, 31-42 and 51-71. Corroboration for the existence of these helices comes from the values of $^3J_{NH\alpha}$, the location of slowly-exchanging NH protons (indicated by closed, shaded and open symbols in the diagram), and the chemical shifts of the αCH protons which tend to shift upfield when involved in a helical structure. The absence of medium-range contacts in the region 72-79, along with rapid NH exchange, was interpreted as indicating an extended structure for this part of the molecule.

5.7.5 Tertiary structure

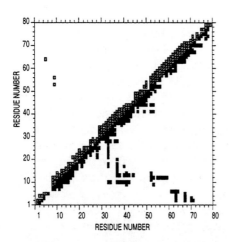

Each filled square represents at least one established connectivity. Above diagonal, main chain connectivities; below diagonal, those involving sidechains.

Lengthy analysis of the 2D and 3D NOESY spectra permitted the initial assignment of 1109 contacts, of which 346 were long-range. The contacts are summarised in the diagram (left): almost all long-range contacts were concentrated in three regions of the molecule,

and indicate contacts between the N-terminal segment and the C-terminal half of helix H3, between helix H1 and the N-terminal segment of helix H3, and between helices H1 and H1' and helix H2. Distance constraints were then set for strong NOE cross-peaks at <2.75Å, medium at<3.75Å, and weak at <5.25 Å; in addition, given the long mixing time of 200 ms for these experiments, an additional class of very weak contacts was introduced at <6 Å. Initial structures were generated using these constraints and the computer program XPLOR, and then an iterative process of refinement followed, with more assignments being added as the structure improved. During this process a few earlier assignments were found to have been wrong, and were corrected, while some new assignments became possible. The final family of 49 structures (left) was the result of 1228 NOE restraints, along with 64 backbone hydrogen bond restraints (from 32 residues) and 76 dihedral angles for the α-helical regions. Energy calculations on this family showed only small values for the notional energy (ΣE_{nmr} – see section 4.11.3) contribution of unfulfilled NOE distance constraints (the NOE pseudo-energy), and no violations of dihedral angle constraints. An averaged structure was produced as shown below.

Above, family of 49 backbone models derived from distance constraints: below, ribbon diagrams of the HMG box 1 fold.

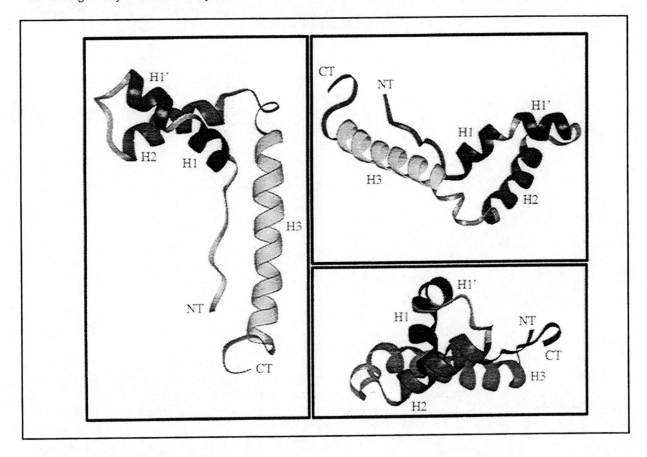

5.8 Limits to growth

The advent of 3D and 4D methods might give the impression that
the progress of NMR to larger and yet larger proteins is inevitable.
Resolution is vastly improved by 4D, and when that begins to run
out, why not extend the methods to 5D and beyond? Unfortunately
there are two reasons why such extrapolations have their limits.
The first is the increasing time taken by multidimensional pulse
sequences, with all their associated phase cycling. At the end of a
sufficiently extended sequence, much or most of the phase coherence will have been lost to transverse relaxation, and there will be
little left to detect. More importantly, correlation times inexorably
get longer with larger molecules, and one by one the smaller
coupling constants become unusable for the production of detectable connectivities. The best current estimate is that a correlation
time of about 20 nanoseconds represents a working upper limit:
this would correspond to a globular protein of perhaps 35 kilodaltons, though in an ideal situation 50 might possibly be reached. Not
all situations are ideal, so in other cases 10-15 kilodaltons might be
the limit. Of course, much useful work can be done on autono-
mously folding domains of larger proteins, and of large but flexible
molecules; significant internal motion will reduce correlation times,
and such molecules might be particularly interesting to study. In
any case the really interesting questions about many molecules are
not answered by the sledgehammer of total structure determination, but by much more subtle experimental design. The growing
use of solid-state NMR, and the study of nucleic acids, carbohydrates, molecular dynamics and molecular interactions will keep
the spectrometers busy for a long time to come; these topics are the
subject of Chapter 6.

CHAPTER 6: BEYOND PROTEIN STRUCTURE

Applications of NMR to other biomolecules and properties

6.1 Molecular dynamics

6.1.1 Molecular Motions

No molecule is ever still. Even at absolute zero, each vibrational motion within a molecule retains a little energy, and at more normal temperatures there is an average of $\frac{1}{2}kT$ (about 2×10^{-21} joules at room temperature) of energy per "degree of freedom" of the molecule. Since a molecule of N atoms has 3N motional degrees of freedom, this represents quite a lot of stored energy, and it is mostly in the form of vibrations – for our N-atom molecule, there are (3N-6) separate vibrational motions. Thus a 200-residue protein, with perhaps 3000 atoms, will be undergoing some 10,000 separate vibrational motions at any one time; their frequencies will range from 10^{13} Hz for the stretching of a carbon-hydrogen bond to very slow oscillations, perhaps 1 Hz, involving the whole molecule. If to these vibrations we add more specific motions, such as the opening and closing of an active site, it becomes clear that no description of a molecule is complete without some indication of its dynamics.

Molecular motions are centrally important to all our thinking about molecules. Function does not follow structure alone, but the combination of structure and dynamics. Further, much of the information derived using NMR is directly or indirectly influenced by atomic and molecular motions; this influence may be informative, or it may deny us potentially valuable data. NMR certainly gives us windows through which we can investigate some types of molecular motion, but it is important to remember that dynamic effects are present whether or not we look for them or take them into account. Acquiring data from a highly mobile molecule and then making it fit a static and rigid model will result in incorrect conclusions, or an incorrect structure; this is an aspect of NMR structural work which is sometimes not taken seriously enough. The NMR effects of molecular motion described below are equally applicable to proteins, nucleic acids or carbohydrates; this section will major on proteins, and further discussion of the dynamics of nucleic acids and carbohydrates will be found in sections 6.2 and 6.3.

6.1.2 Correlation times

In Chapter 2 we discussed the relaxation process, and in particular how relaxation depends on molecular motions via the local "magnetic noise" which they generate. In that discussion molecular motion was defined in terms of a single *correlation time*, described as roughly the time taken for a molecule to translate one molecular diameter or to rotate through one radian. This simplified description conceals a much more complex reality. Each nucleus which we observe is subject to local randomly-fluctuating magnetic fields which are the sum of many separate effects, each with its own frequency, intensity and direction. The analysis of such apparently random fluctuations is always difficult: if the molecule is not spherical, and not rigid, and undergoes a large number of separate internal motions, then it is very difficult to predict a value for the effective correlation time at any nucleus and hence to forecast its relaxation properties. Difficult, but not impossible; a full theoretical treatment, developed by Woessner and refined by a number of workers since, can predict relaxation properties by adding together the effects of many different molecular motions.

It is quite a different matter, however, to reverse the calculations: to take one or two measured quantities such as relaxation times, and derive motions from them. Indeed, it is not possible to derive motions from relaxation measurements at all unless the system is restricted in some way – for example if it can be shown to tumble as a rigid unit – or additional information is available from other sources. This is not to belittle the effort that has gone into the analysis of these phenomena, but simply to point out that only in very special cases, and given considerable computation, can we begin to analyse the detail of molecular motion on the basis of NMR data. The conclusions to be drawn from such analyses will often be fairly general, for example that a correlation time is greater or smaller than some limiting value.

6.1.3 Windows on molecular motion

NMR analysis gives us several windows into the spectrum of molecular motion; the diagram (left) gives an idea of the frequency ranges covered.

(a) *Dynamic effects on signal intensity – hydrogen-deuterium exchange.* Many of the protons in biological molecules are labile – they are in constant exchange with solvent protons at a rate which depends on pH and the accessibility of the proton to solvent. This is true of OH, NH, and SH protons on the backbones and sidechains of proteins,

Windows on molecular motion provided by NMR.

and also of a number of amide NH protons on nucleic acid bases and carbohydrates; the most interesting for our purposes are generally amide protons, which have exchange rates within useful ranges for NMR. Several factors determine whether the resonances of these protons can be of use to us. The first is the condition that the exchange rate must be slow on the NMR timescale – say, less than about 10 s^{-1} – otherwise the resonance of the proton will be merged with that of the solvent (see section 2.13.1). Given this condition, it is then necessary that the "proton" is indeed a proton, i.e. either the solvent is H_2O or, if it is D_2O, that the proton of interest has not already exchanged with deuterium from the solvent. This is where the first important application of labile-proton exchange appears. If we take a protein that has been lyophilised from H_2O, dissolve it in D_2O at around neutral pH, and observe its spectrum immediately, we shall see a number of NH resonances in the spectral region from 7-9 ppm. They will not represent all the NH groups in the molecule, because some will already have exchanged for deuterons by the time we get the sample into the spectrometer, but as the spectrum is observed over a period of time the remaining NH signals will reduce in intensity and eventually disappear. For some this will take minutes, for others hours or even weeks or months, and the relative rates are a measure of the accessibility of each amide proton to solvent. Slow exchange with solvent deuterium may indicate that a proton is buried, or that it is involved in a hydrogen bond, or both. Typically, involving a hydrogen atom in a hydrogen bond may slow its exchange rate with solvent by a factor of about 10^5.

As an alternative to observing slow-exchanging protons by dissolving protonated sample in a deuterated solvent, it is of course possible to observe rapidly-exchanging protons by the converse, dissolving a pre-deuterated protein in H_2O and observing the growing signals of rapidly-exchanged protons in the absence of the others. This method has been used in elegant work on protein folding pathways.

The slow exchange of hydrogen-bonded protons has also been used to advantage in the investigation of tRNA in H_2O solution. In this case all non-hydrogen-bonded labile protons exchange too fast with solvent to be separately observable, while those forming inter-base hydrogen bonds exchange more slowly and appear in the spectrum. Since the chemical shifts of these H-bond protons are characteristic not only of the base pairs they belong to but also of neighbouring base pairs, it becomes possible to assign all the observable NH resonances and measure their exchange times, thus revealing the relative flexibilities and stabilities of different regions of the tRNA molecule.

(b) *Linewidth.* Linewidth in NMR spectra is of course a function of the transverse relaxation time T_2, and hence of molecular motion. Bearing in mind that complex motions cannot be calculated from a single relaxation time, there are nevertheless many examples of the value of linewidths in revealing mobility. In particular there are many large proteins whose size and general rigidity lead to very broad spectral lines and whose spectrum is mostly featureless, but which nevertheless display some sharp resonances. These correspond to regions of the molecule which are much more flexible and free to move than the rest, for example "hinge" regions between domains which are themselves rigid. A good example is the hinge between the stem and head of myosin. Flexible regions on other proteins are often turns which loop out into the solvent; many are associated with antigenicity. Such rather qualitative observations of linewidth suffice for many purposes, if only in establishing the existence of flexible regions in rigid molecules.

(c) *Relaxation measurements*. More quantitative estimates of mobility can of course be made by direct measurement of transverse and longitudinal relaxation times (see Section 3.7), normally of protons. All such measurements are subject to the caveats expressed at the beginning of the section concerning the use of single parameters to estimate complex motions. Now that ^{15}N and ^{13}C-enriched protein samples are more readily available, the determination of relaxation parameters for these isotopes presents another route to the estimation of mobility. Because the relaxation depends mainly on interactions with directly attached protons, ^{13}C and ^{15}N relaxation provide useful windows on protein chain mobility. Preliminary studies on a number of proteins reveal the expected rigid cores, with loops and tails of varying mobility.[†]

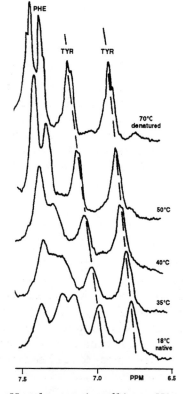

Heat denaturation of histone H1.

(d) *Chemical shift*. The normal chemical shift of a resonance may be perturbed in a number of ways, including the direct effects of protein folding and secondary effects such as paramagnetic shifts and ring-current shifts. If the molecule is rigid, only paramagnetic shifts exhibit temperature dependence, and so any temperature-dependence of shifts in a molecule which is known to lack a paramagnetic centre must indicate that it is not rigid and that structure determination might be difficult. It is, of course, possible to make use of the temperature dependence itself: in the diagram at left the chemical shift of a resonance from the single tyrosine residue in histone H1 shows a temperature dependent shift as the globular region of the molecule melts with increasing temperature. A single resonance is observed because exchange between folded and unfolded states is fast relative to the chemical-shift difference between them. Establishment of the extremes of the shift perturbation to give the "folded" and "unfolded" positions of the resonance then permitted use of the chemical shift as an indicator of equilibrium constant. As a result, a plot of log(shift) against $1/T$ became effectively a van't Hoff plot, from which ΔH for the folding could be determined.

Chemical-shift studies make it clear that proteins differ markedly in their mobility, ranging from those (mostly enzymes) with structures that can be regarded as rigid (though still with many internal vibrations and fluctuations, and some flexibility around recognition sites to permit rapid substrate binding) to those which are almost

[†] See Wagner, G. *Current Opinion in Structural Biology* 3 748-754 (1993)

totally flexible. One way of observing this flexibility within proteins is by the measurement of *ring-flipping rates*. A sidechain ring of phenylalanine should in most circumstances yield five resonances as the local molecular environment differentiates the notionally equivalent 1-H and 5-H (and 2-H and 4-H) protons from each other, giving four resonances to add to that of the 3-H. However, if the ring is flipping rapidly about its bond to the β-carbon, 1-H and 5-H (and 2-H and 4-H) resonances become equivalent and the five resonances will become three. Many studies have shown interesting results using ring-flipping as a probe: for example, tyrosine and phenylalanine residues in lysozyme flip freely, indicating a high degree of internal mobility, while in cytochrome c several freely flipping rings become immobilised on binding the haem group.

(e) *J-values.* J-coupling values are often used in structure determination: as with chemical shift, exchange between conformations will average a J-value. Intermediate values of J (say ≈5 Hz for protons) should thus be regarded with a certain reserve, because they may be simply a motional average. Temperature-dependence studies will often resolve the matter. Reference to the Karplus relationship (see page 28) assures us that extreme values (≈ 10 Hz, or ≈ 0 Hz) are much less likely to be averages and can be interpreted with greater confidence.

(f) *NOE intensities.* Mobile regions of an otherwise rigid molecule give rise to unexpectedly low NOE intensities. Study of the temperature dependence of this effect, and in particular its variation with changing mixing times, can be fruitful. As with any studies dependent on NOE intensities, the contribution of spin diffusion (the spread of magnetisation through a spin system by mechanisms other than NOE effects) must be calculated or ruled out.

6.2 Oligosaccharides

Oligosaccharides have many functions inside and outside cells, and much has yet to be discovered concerning their structure and function. Their influence on cell-cell communication, cell adhesion and on the control of differentiation makes an understanding of carbohydrate recognition vital to our understanding of development and of diseases such as cancer. Enormous biochemical effort has revealed the complex primary structures of monosaccharides and simple oligosaccharides: now NMR promises 3D structures, but not without first facing and overcoming some formidable problems.

The first set of problems is practical. To begin with, there is the nature of the NMR spectrum of a sugar ring. Although the spectrum at left is only that of a disaccharide, sucrose, it illustrates clearly how most of the proton resonances are crowded into a small region between 3 and 5 ppm. Clearly the addition of another half-

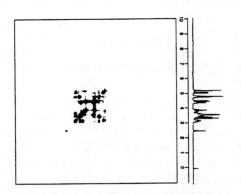

270-Mhz proton spectrum of sucrose illustrates the restricted chemical-shift range of oligosaccharide spectra.

dozen rings will seriously congest this region, and the small range of chemical shifts will complicate assignment. Another serious problem for NMR studies is that the synthesis of carbohydrates, unlike that of proteins or nucleic acids, is not template-driven, and there are as yet no routine methods for synthesising quantities of a particular, possibly branched, oligosaccharide. Thus NMR must be undertaken on the small quantities obtainable in pure form from natural samples; at least 50 nmol is normally required. Purification of these natural products is not at all simple, because naturally-occurring oligosaccharides are often microheterogeneous. To add to these difficulties, the lack of any template to control synthesis precludes isotopic labelling – except by isotopically labelling the whole glycoprotein or glycolipid *in vivo* and cleaving and separating out the resultant oligosaccharides. For all these reasons most NMR studies to date have used proton resonance, with contributions from natural-abundance ^{13}C studies which are particularly valuable because ^{13}C shifts are very sensitive to conformation.

The second set of problems is more fundamental, and concerns the flexibility of oligosaccharide chains. Flexibility, or the lack of it, is of great importance for molecules which are involved in recognition – for example, binding of a flexible chain to a rigid site on a lectin will exact an entropy penalty which influences the stability of the complex, while permitting more rapid binding by permitting multiple binding pathways. Mobility is also very relevant to NMR studies for the reasons outlined at the beginning of this chapter: if the NMR data obtained from the average of a number of conformations is analysed as if they were one rigid structure, the resulting model (called a "virtual structure" by Jardetzky) may be very misleading. Current evidence seems to be that some oligosaccharides (for example some of the blood-group determinants) are indeed rigid, while others appear flexible. The question is – how do you tell? and what constitutes flexibility in this case? Can we assume that an oligosaccharide is a series of essentially rigid units (the sugar rings) joined by flexible links, rather like the peptide backbone of a protein? or is flexibility within sugar rings significant? It appears that at least for pyranosides the rings may be assumed rigid, but all these questions and problems are still being actively addressed.

6.2.1 Approaches to oligosaccharide structure

(a) *Assignment and primary sequence.* The key to assignment in all oligosaccharide studies is the proton H1 (diagrams, left) which is attached to the *anomeric* carbon atom. This proton appears at lower field than the other protons and in addition has J-couplings to its neighbours which can be diagnostic of the monosaccharide type. Given assignments of the anomeric proton, COSY, RELAY and HOHAHA experiments should permit assignment of other ring protons, bearing in mind that each sugar ring is essentially an isolated spin system. Spectrum overlap may be reduced by using homonuclear 3D spectroscopy, especially the HOHAHA-COSY

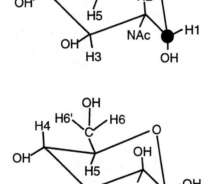

Top: a-D-N-acetylglucosamine (GlcNAc)
Centre: b-D-mannose (Man)
Bottom: a-D-galactose (Gal)
with standard numbering: the anomeric
carbon is indicated by ●.

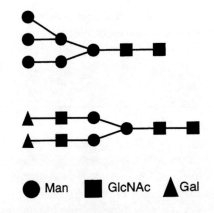

Examples of branching patterns found in oligosaccharide branches of glycoproteins.

● Man   ■ GlcNAc   ▲ Gal

combination in which each slice of data, selected by the shift of its C1 carbon resonance, can contain one complete ring system. Problems may arise from the fact that at least some protons are *strongly coupled* – their J-coupling is of the same order as their chemical shift difference, and this produces intensity distortions (see page 28). Assignments may be confirmed by intra-residue NOESY crosspeaks.

Once resonances within rings have been assigned, the next step is the sequence of the saccharides. If the molecule is related to previously-known structures, one of the most straightforward approaches is the so-called "fingerprint" method – the resonances are compared to those in a database of known spectra. If no similar structures have been determined before, then the analysis must be *ab initio*†. COSY analysis and assignment is followed by the identification of inter-residue NOESY contacts between the anomeric proton on one ring and proton/s on the next. Ring geometry may be determined or confirmed from the values of J-couplings.

(b) *Conformational analysis.* Three-dimensional structure determination depends on the contacts between rings revealed by NOE difference, NOESY or ROESY spectroscopy. Long-range constraints are generally not observed, and indeed the number of constraints available is very small compared with those used for the determination of protein structure. Accordingly protein-type algorithms such as DISGEO do not work effectively for oligosaccharides. The most promising approach seems to be to combine NMR data (constraints and coupling constants) with theoretical energy-minimisation calculations. The most popular of these are the so-called HSEA (Hard-Sphere, Exo-Anomeric) calculations which assume each monosaccharide ring to be rigid and the main sources of energy minimisation to be the angle-dependent potential energy of torsion-angles of the glycosidic linkages, along with van der Waals contributions from atomic contacts. This is a highly simplified model, and not really suitable for the application of molecular dynamics calculations, but has been extensively used. More sophisticated approaches are being developed, using the bond length, bond angle, torsion, van der Waals, electrostatic, H-bond and NOE-constraint terms described for proteins in section 4.11.3: these potentials are more compatible with reliable molecular dynamics calculations. Ideally, such calculations also include the contribution of solvent, but the cost in computing time is very high.

(c) *Molecular motion.* Molecular dynamics calculations under appropriate energy constraints can give us an effective model of molecular motion, so that while we may illustrate the "structure" of an oligosaccharide by a single picture to give us something to think about, we also have a clear notion of the types and frequencies of motion that are going on. Given such a description of the motions, their time-averaged geometry can then be used to back-calculate the NMR spectra as a powerful check on the validity of the models used. The technical difficulty of all this may be daunting, but it is

†Homans, S. *Progress in NMR Spectroscopy* <u>22</u> 55-81 (1990)

clear that an understanding of oligosaccharide structure is vital in molecular biology, and that NMR will be one of the main tools in providing it.

6.3 Nucleic acid conformation

Compared to NMR work on oligosaccharides, investigation of nucleic acids is greatly advantaged by the existence of straightforward procedures to produce quantities of pure and if necessary isotope-labelled sample. However some of the disadvantages and problems reappear: complex molecular motions and a lack of long-range NOE contacts mean that while it is certainly possible to provide good qualitative analysis of local structures and secondary structures, fully reliable and quantitative larger scale structure determinations by NMR remain, for the time being, elusive.

(a) *Assignment.* Assignment of nucleic acid resonances is even more difficult than that for proteins. For a start, there are only four different bases, so each occurs very frequently in any given structure. Each base forms a spin system, and each deoxyribose contains seven protons in another coupled system, and so essentially there are only five independent spin systems repeated many times and distinguished only by chemical shift. Chemical shifts are very dependent on the primary sequence, and additional information will become available if the structure is double-stranded, because each base pair in a sequence is then consistently stacked between two others, and so its shift will be determined by the ring-current effects of both; this gives sixteen different possible environments apart from any lesser conformation-dependent effects. For sequence-dependent assignment, NOESY yields more information than COSY, and so a combination of the two is required for full assignment. The diagram opposite shows the main regions of interest in the COSY and NOESY spectra of oligonucleotides.

(b) *Conformational analysis.* As with proteins, the conformational analysis of a nucleic acid sample relies on J-couplings, on through-space proximity revealed through NOE effects, and to a lesser extent on conformation-dependent chemical shifts.

J-couplings would appear relatively straightforward analytical tools, provided that they can be measured accurately from appropriate 2D spectra. Normal Karplus-type relations apply, and appropriate parameters have been derived for torsion angles in oligonucleotides. Considerable work has also been done on the analysis of ribose sugar-ring conformations via proton-proton J values, and it might be assumed that this would form a reliable basis for analysis, particularly because the two major conformers of a furanose ring, the N-conformer and the S-conformer, have readily distinguished combinations of J-values for the H1´-H2´ and H3´-H4´ couplings. However, it has been pointed out[†] that many

Observable protons in DNA bases (above) and deoxyribose (below). Shaded hydrogen atoms exchange with solvent, though more slowly when hydrogen-bonded.

[†]Van de Ven, F.J.M., Hilbers, C.W., *Eur.J.Biochem.* **178** 1-38 (1988)

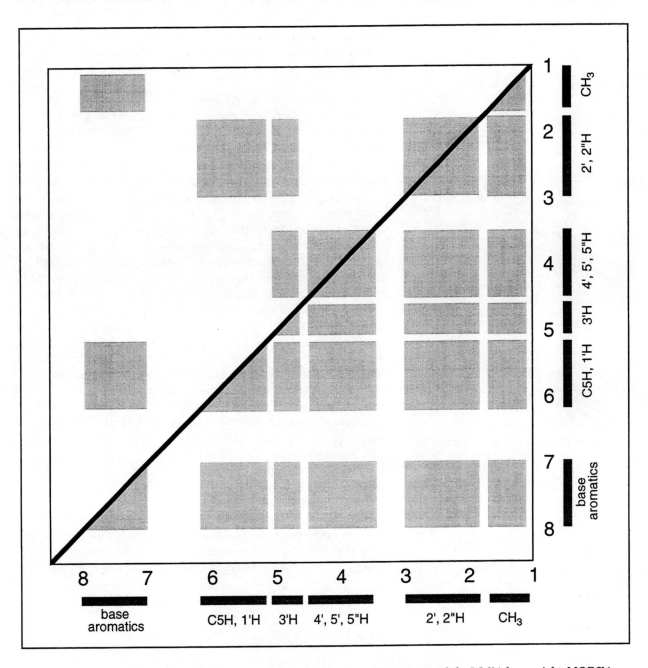

The main connectivity regions found in two-dimensional spectra of DNA: upper left, COSY; lower right, NOESY.

published values for these two constants measured from oligo-nucleotides lie in a region not corresponding to any particular conformer, indicating that the observed value represented a weighted average from two or more conformers in dynamic equilibrium.

Karplus relationships are of limited value in the measurement of backbone torsion angles because there is a distinct scarcity of proton-proton couplings, forcing the use of proton-to-phosphorus coupling constants for torsion angles β and ε, with ^{13}C - ^{31}P couplings to constrain the value of ε. There are, however, no couplings at all to determine the angles α and ζ of the O-P bonds, and so phosphorus chemical shift is the only available guide.

Determination of distance constraints in oligonucleotides using nuclear Overhauser effects presents a number of problems not normally encountered in work with proteins. Partly this results from the need to determine distances more accurately: there are fewer constraints available, and virtually none are long-range, so conformation must be determined more exactly at a local level. At first sight this might seem straightforward: a number of known interproton distances, fixed by covalent bonding, might be expected to provide yardsticks for the determination of unknown distances. Examples are the H5-H6 interproton distance of cytosine (=2.48 Å) and the H2´-H2″ distance in deoxyribose (=1.8 Å). Unfortunately there are problems with this approach, too, because there are many pathways for spin-diffusion in the closely-coupled spin systems of sugars and bases. If spin-diffusion spreads magnetisation through the system during the mixing time for NOE measurements, the effect is to make all the NOE's appear identical, so all distances seem equal to the "yardstick" distance. In less extreme cases, distances longer than the yardstick would be underestimated and shorter ones overestimated. Reducing mixing times to help overcome these effects has the undesirable result of reducing all the NOE intensities and hence the precision with which they can be measured.

As a result of these limitations, the most successful NMR studies of oligonucleotides to date have been those which define relatively small structures such as hairpins or unusual constructions such as four-stranded telomeric structures. Up to perhaps 20 bases, RNA structures determined by NMR can perhaps rival those from x-ray measurements, but there is still a long way to go before nucleic acid structures can be tackled with the same confidence as proteins.

6.4 Solid-state NMR and the magic angle

One-dimensional NMR spectra of solids look quite different from the high-resolution solution spectra described in Chapters 2 and 3; the spectral lines are very much broader and differently shaped. Of course, the linewidths obtained from solids would be expected to be greater than those from liquids simply because of the much shorter T_2 transverse relaxation time caused by the restricted motion of the molecules, but the chief reasons for the differences are other effects, notably *dipole-dipole interactions* and *chemical shift anisotropy*. These could safely be omitted from the earlier discussion because, although they are present in solution, they average to zero and so can be discounted in considering solution spectra. For solid-state NMR, however, they become dominant.

Dipole-dipole interaction is, as its name suggests, the direct effect of the magnetic moment of one nucleus on that of another. The result is similar to the spin-spin splitting described earlier, but much stronger; it falls away rapidly with distance, being inversely dependent on the cube of the distance between the nuclei, so is only really important for pairs of nuclei which are directly bonded to each other or are nearest neighbours, and which both have non-zero magnetic moments. The most important property of the dipole-dipole interaction from our point of view is that it is *anisotropic* – that is, the splitting depends on the orientation (relative to the applied field B_o) of the vector joining the two nuclei. In solutions where the molecules are tumbling rapidly, this directional effect averages to zero, but in a solid the molecules are fixed. If the solid is crystalline or otherwise oriented in some way, useful information may be obtained from changes in the splitting pattern as the crystal orientation is altered relative to B_o. If the solid is amorphous, and all orientations are present, the resulting sum of many different dipolar splittings is a very broad resonance.

The way of minimising the effect of dipole-dipole coupling is essentially the same as that used to minimise normal (scalar) spin-spin splitting: *spin decoupling*. Continuous irradiation in the Larmor frequency band of one nucleus effectively decouples it from the other by causing it to undergo rapid transitions. Fortunately, most of the important cases – for example, carbon-hydrogen interactions – involve nuclei whose Larmor frequencies are quite different in a given applied field, so the decoupling frequency is well away from the detection frequency. Decoupling power required to be effective in a solid is quite high: up to perhaps 100 watts may be needed, far more than the power used in high-resolution spin-decoupling experiments. Application of decoupling power narrows the NMR spectrum of a solid, but spectra are still typically many kilohertz wide and fairly featureless: this residual spectrum width is caused by *chemical shift anisotropy*.

In Box 2.2, it was pointed out that the diamagnetic effect which gives rise to chemical shift is, like dipole-dipole interactions, dependent on the orientation of the molecule relative to the applied magnetic field. In solution these directional effects are averaged by molecular motion to give the observed high-resolution chemical shifts which are so useful in solution NMR. In the solid state this averaging effect cannot take place, and so the chemical shift anisotropy gives rise to chemical shifts and lineshapes which depend on orientation relative to B_o. An amorphous solid, with spin decoupling applied to remove dipole-dipole broadening, gives a typical spectrum lineshape as shown in the diagram (left, centre). It is possible to remove this broadening: the method is to *spin the sample* at high speed about an axis at the so-called *magic angle* relative to B_o. The reason lies in the mathematical description of the effect of spinning: if the sample is spinning about an axis which makes an angle of θ with the direction of B_o, line-broadening depends on $(3\cos^2\theta-1)$. If $\cos^2\theta=0.33$, this term disappears. The angle whose cosine is 0.577 (corresponding to $\cos^2\theta=0.33$) is 54.7°,

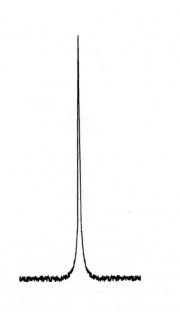

Spectra of a solid: top, too broad to see: middle, with dipolar decoupling: bottom, with decoupling and magic-angle spinning.

so this becomes the magic angle. Spinning the sample at very high speed (up to some kilohertz) about an axis at 54.7° to the applied field, while simultaneously applying dipolar decoupling, will reduce the linewidths of the spectrum of a solid to those expected from the transverse relaxation time, giving something approaching a high-resolution spectrum (previous page, bottom diagram).

The one remaining problem in solid-state NMR is that of sensitivity. Although transverse relaxation times for solids are very short, longitudinal relaxation times are very long because there is no efficient mechanism for the spin systems to exchange energy with their surroundings. Since the spin system must be allowed to relax completely before the pulse cycle is repeated, the time between successive pulse cycles must be long and collecting data from solid samples becomes a very lengthy process. The situation is worse if, for example, the nucleus being observed is rare, such as natural-abundance carbon-13. In such cases a technique known as *cross-polarisation* becomes useful. A pulse at the ^1H frequency is followed by a spin-locking proton signal, and then by a pulse at carbon-13 frequency. If the strengths of the pulses are correctly chosen, the *Hartmann-Hahn condition* (see Section 4.9) is fulfilled and coherence is transferred very efficiently to the carbon nuclei. The result is an enhancement (in the case of protons and carbon) of about four times in the detectable signal, and therefore a factor of sixteen in the time taken to collect it. Of course, usually solids are stable: stability over time means that at least the sample will remain in good condition even if several days are needed to collect the spectra.

For many years, solid-state NMR has rarely been applied to biological samples. In part this was (and still is) due to the need for fairly large homogeneous solid samples and to their cost if isotopic labelling is required. However, work has begun recently on a number of new approaches, particularly in the area of membranes and membrane-protein interactions. It is possible to make an oriented sample of membrane bilayer by evaporating from organic solvent onto a flat surface, and such surfaces used singly or in a stack can provide enough oriented sample to give useful spectra. Recent examples[†] include work on gramicidin and on fd viral coat protein in membranes.

6.5 NMR of lipids and membranes

Membranes present a unique set of problems to the NMR spectroscopist. Complex and subtle, combining structure with fluidity, and containing many different protein as well as lipid components, for many scientists membrane structure has presented a challenge too great. Nevertheless substantial progress has been made in the investigation of membrane structure and dynamics, much of it using *electron spin resonance*, which is beyond the scope of this book.

†McConnell, P.A. et al., *J.Mol.Biol.* 233 447-463 (1993)

Ketchem, R.R., Hu,W., Croos, T.A., *Science* 261 1457-1460 (1993)

Real membranes are not very suitable candidates for NMR studies: they contain too many different components and a range of more-fluid and less-fluid regions which between them preclude detailed spectrum analysis. Most NMR studies have thus concentrated on model systems consisting of one or a few lipid components with, if required, a single type of protein incorporated into the structure. Given a suitable system, a major consideration is then the form which the model membrane assumes. A membrane bilayer can be prepared in the form of small closed vesicles by sonication; such small structures can tumble in solution sufficiently fast to produce high-resolution spectra, but suffer the disadvantage that the packing of the phospholipid chains is not typical of a natural membrane which is much more nearly flat.

The alternative to using small vesicles is to allow the formation of larger structures and to apply the techniques of solid-state NMR to provide detailed information about internuclear distances. Solid-state methods have employed ^{31}P resonance of the polar headgroups of membrane phospholipids to investigate phase changes between the different liquid-crystal forms, or have been applied to systems which have been selectively labelled with isotopes such as ^{13}C or deuterium. The deuterium nucleus has a spin quantum number of 1, and so exhibits nuclear resonance between three nuclear energy levels; deuterium resonance is not suitable for most high-resolution studies of biomolecules and is rarely used outside the study of membranes. In this application, however, it is very useful: the broad-line deuterium spectrum obtained from selectively labelled lipids shows splittings which are diagnostic of molecular motion in the lipid chains. It is thus possible to study mobility gradients along lipid chains, order-disorder transitions, diffusion of lipids in the fluid membrane structure, and the effect of the presence of membrane proteins on lipid diffusion.

A more recent development has been that of *rotational resonance NMR*. This technique employs the experimental methods of solid-state NMR, but with the refinement that the rate of magic-angle spinning is variable. Samples are specifically labelled with, say, ^{13}C or ^{15}N at two sites assumed fairly close to each other. The dipolar coupling between the two nuclei is then *selectively* restored when the magic-angle spinning frequency is equal to the chemical-shift difference between the two nuclei or a small multiple of it. Since the coupling itself is distance-dependent, the method provides a sensitive way of measuring internuclear distances.

As with every other area of NMR investigation, work on membranes and their associated proteins is producing a stream of technical advances which shows no sign of drying up. Spectroscopic ingenuity and a steadily expanding repertoire of sample-preparation and isotopic labelling methods will make this a fruitful field for investment of research effort.

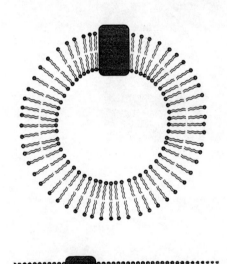

High-resolution spectra can be obtained from lipids or proteins in small vesicles (above): larger bilayers (below) need solid-state NMR techniques.

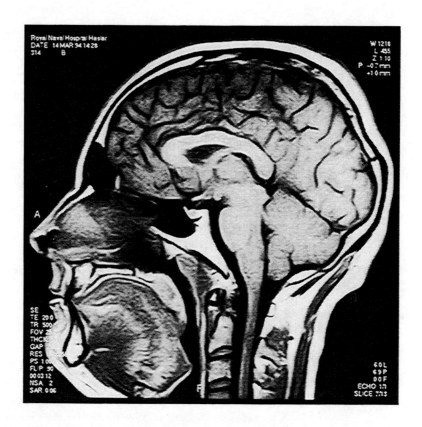

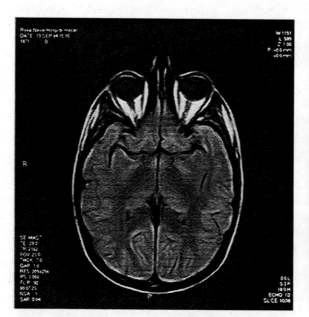
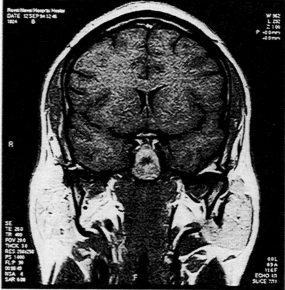

MRI images of the human head. Top, sagittal section: bottom left, transverse section: bottom right, coronal section.
Images by courtesy of Surgeon-Commander Jeremy Hogg, RNH Haslar.

CHAPTER 7: MAGNETIC RESONANCE IMAGING

Medical and in-vivo applications of NMR

7.1 NMR imaging – theory

Most of the applications of NMR we have discussed so far have been applicable almost exclusively in scientific research. In this last chapter we move out of the laboratory and into the hospital, where magnetic resonance methods are contributing very powerful imaging and diagnostic tools. In the first part of this chapter we consider *MRI*, or magnetic resonance imaging (formerly also called NMR tomography or zeugmatography) which provides an image of the internal organs. The final section (7.8) briefly describes *MRS*, which simply stands for magnetic resonance spectroscopy but is conventionally used to describe the production of an NMR spectrum *in vivo* from a selected region within the organism using a radiofrequency coil on the surface. MRI and MRS employ phenomena that are already familiar to us, with one exception: the application of *magnetic field gradients* to encode position information in the detected resonance signal.

The aim of all diagnostic methods is the reliable detection of disease. To do this by an imaging method requires first that we visualise a selected region of the body, representing some measurable property by intensity or by colour on a screen or photograph. This image will be made up of a number of picture elements or *pixels*; the intensity or colour of each pixel represents the value of the measured property within a small volume element (or *voxel*) of the patient's body. Typically, an MRI image will be 256 x 256 pixels, equivalent to pixels 1 mm square on a 25 cm square image. Once visualised, the image will need to be analysed by someone skilled in recognising the difference between images of normal and of diseased tissue.

Clearly for medical diagnosis it is necessary to collect data for an image in a reasonably short time; given the inherent insensitivity of NMR, this means that we must use it in the most efficient way. The most readily detectable nucleus is the proton; the commonest compound in the body is water. Accordingly NMR imaging in clinical practice is performed almost exclusively on the protons of water in body tissues. We may use three main properties of water to produce *contrast*, that is to differentiate one region of an image from another: the *spin density*, or amount of water (hence number of protons) per unit volume, and the *longitudinal relaxation time* T_1, and *transverse relaxation time* T_2. Other NMR parameters such as spin coupling or chemical shift are in general not useful in this context. Spin density and relaxation times vary with tissue type and age; some idea of the range of variation may be seen in the diagram at left.

Measurement of signal intensity and relaxation times for a "normal" NMR sample is a straightforward process. The problem for image formation is the measurement of these properties for a given small volume element within the patient without interference from neighbouring regions. Like so many other problems in NMR, this has been solved in a large number of ingenious ways, many of them now of only historical interest. All of them, however, are founded on a common principle: that of the *magnetic field gradient*.

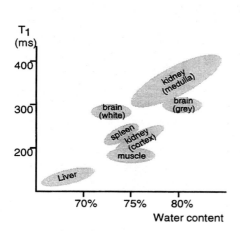

How water content and T_1 vary for different tissues of the rat.

7.2 Methods for localising an NMR signal.

7.2.1 Foundation idea 1: Magnetic field gradients

The magnet in any NMR spectrometer is built with enormous care to ensure that it produces the most uniform field possible: the reason, of course, is that Larmor frequency is proportional to field strength, and it is important that all the nuclei in a sample are in the same magnetic field if any meaningful measurements of chemical shift are to be obtained. However, if chemical shift is of no interest to us because we are using a single resonance – that of the protons of water – for our image, then we can make use of the dependence of Larmor frequency on applied field to provide us with other information. The idea is straightforward: if in addition to the main uniform field within the magnet we impose a much weaker *gradient* of magnetic field which varies linearly from one region of the sample to another, then obviously nuclei in one part of the sample will have a different Larmor frequency from identical nuclei in another part. Further, the Larmor frequency will vary in a linear way from one part of the sample to another such that *the Larmor frequency of any nucleus will tell us where it is along the gradient*. In other words, frequency encodes information about position.

A simple example is shown in the diagrams opposite. A sample consists of two tubes of water, and a field gradient is imposed as shown. A pulse of RF is applied and the resulting FID is transformed in the usual way. The spectrum obtained would have a single peak if no gradient were present, for all we would see would

Magnetic field gradients

be the spectrum of water; however in the presence of the gradient the Larmor frequencies vary linearly across the whole sample, and so the spectra appear as shown below. Although like all spectra they are simply plots of intensity against frequency, each spectrum can now be interpreted as a plot of intensity against *distance*, since distance and frequency are proportional to each other in the presence of the gradient. Thus we have in effect plots of the amount of water present as a function of distance along the gradient axis — each spectrum is a sort of one-dimensional image of the sample.

One way of turning this data into a proper image is to repeat the experiment many times with the gradient in a large number of slightly different directions, collecting spectra which are projections of the sample on a variety of different axes (diagram, below). Given a full set of such data from all directions, a computer can be then used to reconstruct a two-dimensional cross-section of the original sample. Software for doing this already exists in the form of the programmes used to reconstruct images from a series of x-ray images to form the so-called CAT (computer-assisted tomography) scans in common use for medical diagnosis. When applied to NMR, the technique is called the *projection-reconstruction method*; however, it is not used in routine medical magnetic resonance imaging because Fourier methods similar to those used in 2D spectroscopy are much more powerful. Fourier methods are described after the next section, in section 7.2.3.

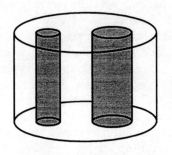

A simple object for imaging – two tubes of water in a holder.

7.2.2 Foundation idea 2: Slice selection

As described above, the projection-reconstruction method forms an image in two dimensions with no reference to the third; although the image would look like a slice through the sample, in fact it

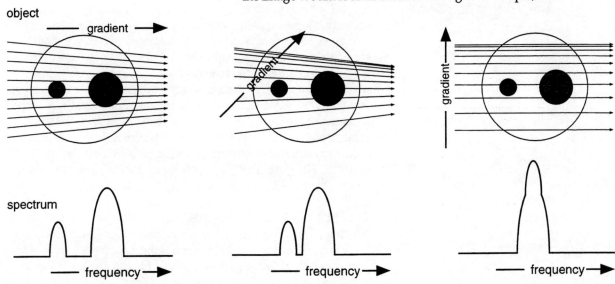

When an FID is collected from our model object in a field gradient, the frequencies appearing in the spectrum indicate the positions of the water tubes relative to the gradient. Data collected like this would enable an image to be reconstructed.

Sketch of a sinc-shaped pulse: in practice there would be far more cycles of radiofrequency within the overall envelope.

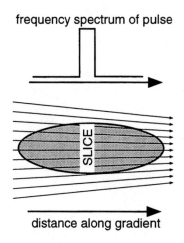

The spectrum of frequencies in a sinc-shaped pulse (above) excites spins in a slice of sample in a field gradient (below).

would contain information from the whole depth of the sample (as into the page). This is acceptable if the sample is two uniform tubes of water, but in a more complex sample it is clearly necessary to image only a particular, selected slice. The way of doing this also depends on field gradients.

Again, the idea is straightforward. In the presence of a uniform gradient, a *selective* pulse is applied. A selective pulse is one which contains only a narrow range of frequencies, and so excites only those spins in a slice, perpendicular to the applied field gradient, which corresponds to a particular Larmor frequency. As discussed in Chapter 2, short pulses tend to contain a wide range of frequencies, so one obvious way of exciting only a narrow range would be to prolong the pulse. Long pulses, however, present all sorts of problems, and there is a better way. The spectrum of frequencies contained in a pulse can be controlled and held to a narrow range if the pulse can be appropriately *shaped*, its growth and decay occurring in a predetermined manner. Clues to the best shape may be found at the bottom of page 23 and the top of page 24: because the square function and the sinc function form a Fourier transform pair, a *sinc-shaped* pulse will have a square spectrum – a spectrum which is confined to a narrow range of frequencies, and with a sharp cutoff at either end of that range. This sharp cutoff means that the nuclei excited in a field gradient will all be in a slice, with a controllable thickness and a sharp cutoff either side. In practice, only three (or at most five) lobes of the sinc function, lasting a total of perhaps 3-5 milliseconds, are needed for a workable slice-selection pulse.

7.2.3 Forming the image

Once a slice has been selected, all the spins in that slice have been excited and are precessing together in the usual way in the main, uniform, magnetic field. What follows is very similar in concept to the stages in the formation of a conventional two-dimensional spectrum described in Chapter 4. After the first excitation, the magnetisation is allowed to evolve for a period of time during which it is effectively labelled with its current Larmor frequency, and then the system is changed in some way and the new Larmor frequencies are detected by collecting the free induction decay. The experiment is then repeated a number of times, for example with a set of varying evolution times, to build up a two-dimensional matrix of FID data. Two Fourier transformations then reveal the Larmor frequencies corresponding to the two stages.

To perform Fourier imaging in two dimensions, a slice is first selected in the presence of, say, a *z-gradient*. This gradient is then switched off, and the magnetisation is then allowed to evolve for a period of time t_1 in the presence of a *y-gradient*, so that nuclei in the slice become labelled with a frequency which reflects their position in the y direction. This is often known as the frequency-labelling or phase-encoding stage. The y-gradient is then switched off, an *x-gradient* is applied, and data is collected (the data readout stage).

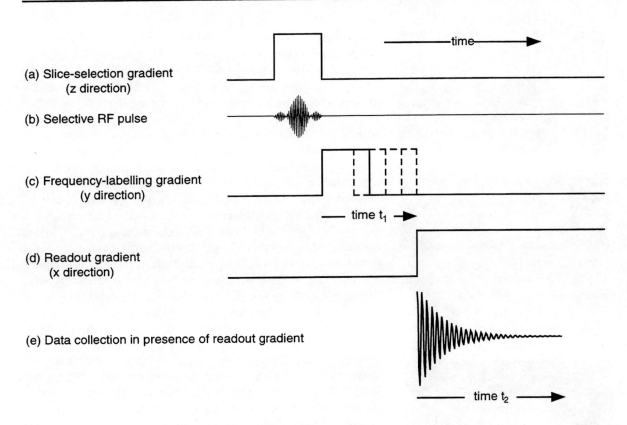

(a) Slice-selection gradient
    (z direction)

(b) Selective RF pulse

(c) Frequency-labelling gradient
    (y direction)

(d) Readout gradient
    (x direction)

(e) Data collection in presence of readout gradient

Schematic of a simple Fourier imaging programme – see text opposite and below.

The Larmor frequencies in the data collected will depend on the position of the nuclei in the x-direction, but labelled with their position in the y-direction. The time t_1 can then be varied systematically, exactly as in 2D NMR spectroscopy, to yield the matrix of data points; the difference is that the frequencies represented in the matrix are indicative of position within the slice rather than chemical shift. Thus two Fourier transforms performed on the data give a two-dimensional "spectrum" which is actually a *map of proton density* as a function of position – in other words, the image of the slice.

In practice, the variation of t_1 to produce the matrix of data is not the best way to achieve the desired result. So much is going on in the sample in terms of relaxation effects that variations in the time taken for each slice-selection-evolution-collection cycle can lead to distortions in the image. To avoid varying t_1 and still produce the same effect, it is possible instead to vary the *strength* of the y-gradient. A little thought will reveal that a strong gradient applied for a short time is equivalent to a weaker gradient applied for a longer time in terms of the phase change encoded across the sample. Thus it is possible to produce an exactly equivalent matrix of data if, rather than varying t_1 for a fixed gradient strength, the strength of the gradient is varied and t_1 is held constant. This so-called *spin-warp* technique is the basis for most practical imaging.

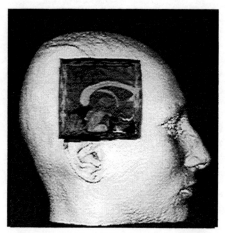

Three-dimensional image with cutaway display: this image was acquired using a fast data-collection method known as MP-RAGE in about 6 minutes.
(Image courtesy of Siemens plc Medical Engineering)

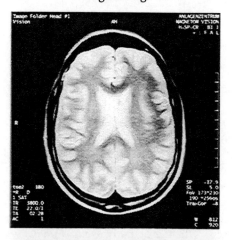

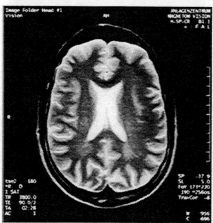

Contrast variation by T_1- and T_2-weighting. Top, TE=22ms, bottom, TE=90 ms.
(Image courtesy of Siemens plc Medical Engineering)

Perhaps 80% of all medical imaging is carried out by the slice-selection, two-dimensional imaging method just outlined. However, just as in conventional NMR spectroscopy, it is possible to take the step from two to three dimensions, and three-dimensional imaging is also used in practice. Generalising the imaging technique to three dimensions is analogous to the construction of a normal 3D NMR spectrum, involving three rather than two Fourier transformations. An initial non-selective 90° pulse (exciting all spins in the whole volume, not just a slice) is applied in the presence of a steady field gradient in the x direction. The magnetisation is allowed to evolve for a period of time t_1; it is now frequency-labelled at a frequency which corresponds to its position along the x-axis. The x-gradient is turned off, and a y-gradient is applied for a time t_2; the frequency labelling now corresponds to the position in both x and y directions. Finally, a z-gradient replaces the y-gradient and the FID is collected during time t_3. The frequency detected during t_3 for any given spin depends, of course, on its location in the z direction, but the signals are also labelled with the x and y coordinates. The signal is a function $s(t_1,t_2,t_3)$ and data is collected systematically, a set of n t_2 values for each of n t_1 values (as before, the dataset may in practice be built up by varying gradient strengths rather than times). If n data points are collected during t_3, we end up with an (nxnxn) matrix of data points. Three Fourier transforms can then be used to recover the data, which is a 3D "map" of proton density in the computer's memory, from which any slice can be sampled for viewing. The advantage of this dataset is that all the data are present: if the physician needs a slice at an unusual angle, it can be retrieved and displayed without further data collection. The disadvantage is the time taken to collect nxnxn FID's – 128x128x128 is just over two million!

7.3 Contrast in NMR imaging

7.3.1 pulses in practice

The most commonly applied pulse regimes in practice are based on the two-dimensional spin-warp variant of Fourier imaging, described above. There are then two commonly used methods of data acquisition – the *gradient echo* and *spin echo* methods. In the gradient echo method, the final (readout) gradient is not simply switched on, but starts with a strong negative excursion. This dephases the spins systematically across the gradient, which is then reversed and held steady at a smaller value while the dephased spins come back into phase to produce an echo which is collected and stored. The time between the centre of the original pulse of radiofrequency and the final echo depends on the values set up for the read gradient, and is called the *echo time* TE. Images formed with larger values of TE have their contrast weighted by the transverse relaxation time T_2; in

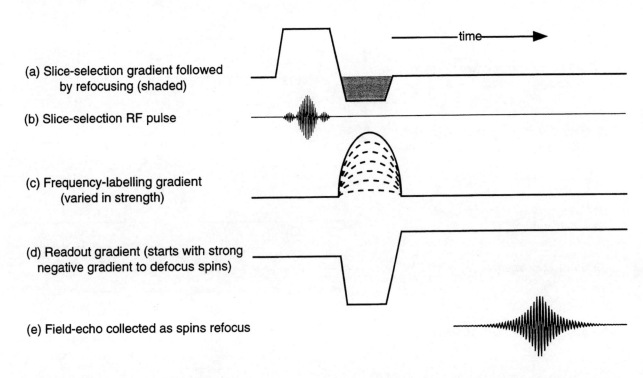

(a) Slice-selection gradient followed by refocusing (shaded)

(b) Slice-selection RF pulse

(c) Frequency-labelling gradient (varied in strength)

(d) Readout gradient (starts with strong negative gradient to defocus spins)

(e) Field-echo collected as spins refocus

Schematic of gradient-echo data collection. Note the variation of strength of the frequency-labelling gradient, and the gradual build-up of each gradient (it is not possible to switch on a magnetic field instantaneously). Note also that it is often possible to overlap gradients in time, thus reducing the total repeat time TR.

other words the contrast of the image is strongly influenced by the T_2 value of the water as well as its spin density at a particular point. TE is normally less than 120 milliseconds.

The time taken for one complete repeat of the select-evolve-collect cycle is called the *repeat time* TR. The total time taken to collect an image depends on TR: if a 256 x 256 image is required, the time taken to collect the data will be 256TR, and so it is important to minimise it. Images taken at short TR values tend to be T_1 weighted. Naturally, TR is always longer than TE.

The basic gradient echo experiment produces the shortest data collection times but gradient echoes do not refocus coherence lost through magnetic field inhomogeneities; high-quality images tend to be collected using a different variant, *spin-echo* imaging (diagram overleaf). In this method, instead of relying on a negative excursion of the read gradient to produce the conditions for an echo, a 180° non-selective pulse is applied just before or just after the phase-encoding gradient. The spin-echo will then appear at time TE where the time between the 90° and the 180° pulses is TE/2. The weighting of the image is then determined by this gap – longer gaps are used for T_2 weighting, shorter for T_1, with TE in the range 15-150 milliseconds. TR for a spin-echo image is in the range of 1.5-2 seconds, giving an acquisition time for a high-quality 256 x 256 pixel image of 5-8 minutes.

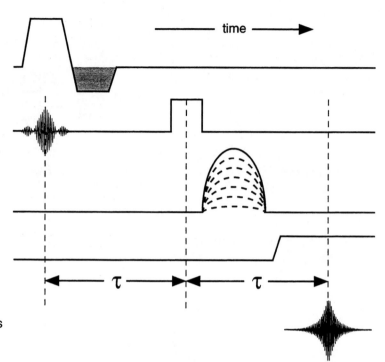

(a) Slice-selection gradient followed by refocusing (shaded)

(b) Slice-selection RF pulse followed after time τ by non-selective 180° pulse

(c) Frequency-labelling gradient (varied in strength)

(d) Readout gradient

(e) Spin-echo collected as spins refocus

Schematic of spin-echo data collection. The 180° non-selective pulse (line b) inverts all spins to produce an echo as described on page 40, and long echo times TE (=2τ) produce a T_2-weighted image. The spin-echo method cancels out many magnetic field imperfections, which helps to produce "clean" images.

In clinical practice, the precise balance of experimental conditions chosen depends strongly on the types of normal and abnormal tissue being investigated. The operator will probably begin with a gradient-echo localising scan to ensure that the correct region is being imaged, and will then select TR and TE for a spin-echo image according to the type of image weighting required. Automated pulse and gradient programmers in the imager will then select appropriate gradient strengths and times for the most efficient collection of data.

7.3.2 Contrast agents

One of the main advantages of MRI over computerised tomography (CT) scanning using x-rays is that the magnetic resonance image is determined by a number of separate parameters; the spin density, relaxation times T_1 and T_2, and diffusion properties of water in different tissues all contribute to image contrast, and a skilled operator can vary experimental parameters such as TR and TE to produce the most effective distinction between abnormal and normal tissue. However, such optimisation can be time-consuming, and a patient may not appreciate lengthy periods in the magnet; in addition, machine time is expensive. These factors account for the increasing use of contrast agents for MRI. The function of a contrast agent is to alter some measurable property differently in normal and abnormal tissue, or between the tissues of different organs, rather in the way that a radio-opaque material (e.g. a barium meal) is used for x-radiography. The requirements for a contrast agent for use in medical applications are stringent:

(a) it must affect contrast efficiently, controllably and repeatably,

(b) it should permit some degree of targeting,

(c) it must be stable, both on the shelf and *in vivo* while the imaging is performed,

(d) after imaging is complete it must be excreted from the body as rapidly and completely as possible,

and of course

(e) it must not be toxic.

Of the many contrast-enhancing mechanisms that can be envisaged, only one has yet found general acceptance. This is the *proton relaxation enhancement* produced by paramagnetic elements; the large magnetic moments of such ions, tumbling rapidly in solution, produce random magnetic noise which shortens the relaxation times of water protons in their vicinity. Paramagnetism is strongest in the transition metals Mn, Fe, Co, Ni, Cu, and the lanthanides Eu, Gd, Tb and Dy. The toxicity of all these elements means that they can only be useful in clinical applications if they are in the form of stable compounds. The first such compound to be awarded U.S. Food and Drug Administration approval was a chelated compound of gadolinium, Gd-DTPA (Gadolinium diethylene triamine penta-acetic acid). This fulfils the criteria outlined above: it is stable in the body and is excreted rapidly via the kidneys, more than half of the agent being cleared by 100 minutes after administration. Gd-DTPA is now commonly used in imaging of the brain, with up to a gram of gadolinium being injected intravenously as Gd-DTPA. The use of such contrast agents is restricted to certain types of case: they are particularly useful in imaging of blood vessels in the brain, in investigations of kidney function and in diagnosis of malignancies which may take up contrast agent more quickly than normal tissue.

7.3.3 A problem with fat

In all the preceding discussion we have assumed that all the signal contributing to an MRI image comes from water, and hence has a single chemical shift. On this assumption any variation of spectral frequency in a field gradient is a clear indicator of position in the slice selected. However, in some tissues which contain a high proportion of fat, significant signal intensity comes from the protons of the hydrocarbon chains of the fat itself. This signal has a chemical shift differing from that of water by about 150 Hz per tesla of applied field, and the signal from fat is thus interpreted during signal processing as coming from a point several pixels displaced from the water image. This effect can be confusing in diagnosis, for example where the perinephritic fat which surrounds the kidneys produces a displaced image. Appropriate spin-conditioning pulse sequences may be used to saturate the fat signal, or to selectively excite fat protons and process them with an allowance for their chemical shift, so producing correctly superimposed images from fat and water protons.

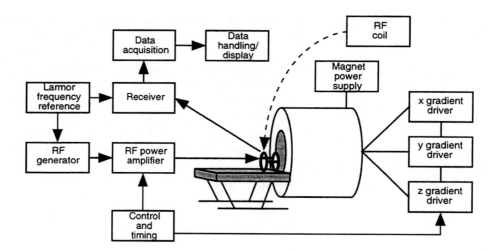

Schematic of an MRI imager. The radiofrequency side of the machine has essentially the same components as a high-resolution spectrometer. For clarity the RF coil is shown outside the magnet.

7.4 MRI practicalities

7.4.1 Instrumentation

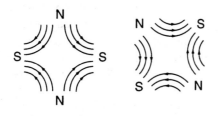

Quadrupole fields like these, added to linear fields, produce uniform gradients.

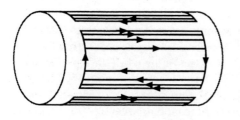

Coils of this form produce quadrupole fields.

Main magnets for MRI are usually superconducting, though generally with smaller fields than those used for high-resolution spectroscopy where resolution depends on having the highest possible field. Fields from 0.5 to 2 tesla are common, though there is an increasing market for low-field machines based on permanent magnets of about 0.2 tesla. The requirements for field homogeneity are not as stringent as those for high resolution spectroscopy, though still very demanding because of the large volume within the magnet: perhaps one part in 10^4 or 10^5 is necessary over the whole volume. On top of this, of course, must come the field gradients of perhaps 5 millitesla per metre. Gradients must be linear, and are produced by special coils operated independently of the main magnet, varying the currents in the coils to control the gradients. The general principle is that a field gradient may be created as the sum of a uniform field and a *quadrupole* field such as that shown in the diagrams (left): by varying the direction of the quadrupole field, x- or y-gradients can be produced with the same main field. The currents through gradient coils may need to be quite high, and are subject to a requirement that they can be switched on and off very quickly – within 500 microseconds – to enable the collection of data in different gradients. This switching requirement places very heavy loads on the power supplies for gradient coils and also puts physical stresses on the coils themselves which may result in vibrating sensations for the patient, so where fast switching is not essential, such as for the variable phase-encoding gradient, gradients are switched more slowly.

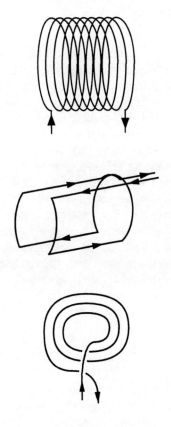

Basic geometries for RF coils. From top: solenoidal, saddle-shaped and flat surface coil.

RF transmitter and receiver coils may be the same coil or two separate coils, sometimes mutually perpendicular, and will be different according to the part of the body being imaged. Specific coils are available for best-quality imaging of localised regions of the spine, the head and neck, breasts, and limbs. In each case the ability to fill the coil with the body part, or to place the coil close to the surface, increases the efficiency and uniformity of spin excitation. Coils fall into three main types: solenoidal, saddle-shaped, or flat surface coils as sketched in the diagrams (left). The radiofrequency power for MRI needs to be high (100 watts to several kilowatts) because of the large sample volumes to be irradiated.

7.4.2 Installation

The siting and installation of an MRI facility depends on a number of factors. Apart from obvious considerations such as accessibility for efficient portering, the most important are to do with minimising the interactions between the separate components (RF, magnet, computers, power supplies) of the spectrometer, and between the spectrometer and its local environment. All strong magnets produce stray fields to some extent, and these fields will have a number of effects: they obviously affect ferromagnetic materials such as passing hospital trolleys, and may also wipe information from magnetic computer storage discs or credit cards. A local field can also deflect the electron beam in a cathode-ray tube such as a computer display, and much modern medical equipment such as gamma cameras and linear accelerators can be affected by magnetic fields. Conversely, of course, changes in ambient magnetic fields due to movement of metallic objects in the neighbourhood of the imaging magnet can alter its own field homogeneity. Similar considerations apply to the radiofrequency radiation utilised by the MRI machine: an unshielded local RF source picked up by the receiver coils of the imager can give rise to a bright spot on the image. Thus an imager must be very carefully sited: the cheapest solution, to put it in a separate building well away from all potential sources of interference, will not often be practicable or desirable. It is possible to shield a magnet by surrounding it with a room sized shell of ferromagnetic material (often iron or steel) but the design of such shells is complex and they are heavy, consisting of plates of steel up to 5 cm thick. A suitable compromise is often to build an MRI facility in a single-story extension to an existing hospital building, linked by a corridor which puts a little distance between the two; in such cases little or no shielding may be needed. All the above problems are minimised, of course, by using smaller magnetic fields, and this adds to the popularity of low-field (0.2 tesla) permanent-magnet machines.

7.4.3 Contra-indications

There are some patients for whom the long period of time spent lying still in the confined space of a magnet is in itself a contra-indication: young children or disturbed patients may not be able to meet this condition without anaesthesia, and others may find the magnet claustrophobic. The main contra-indication on safety grounds is the presence of ferromagnetic material within or around the patient: surgical clips of any kind, metal fragments such as shrapnel, some prostheses, cardiac pacemakers or nerve stimulators are all reasons for not subjecting the patient to a high magnetic field. In addition ferromagnetic objects such as keys or penknives can become very dangerous projectiles in a strong field, and a suitable protocol needs to be established for making everyone, patients, visitors, operators and porters, divest themselves of all such objects before approaching the magnet room. These restrictions may make it difficult to perform MRI on a patient who needs some support system such as infusion or respiration, as it may not be possible to permit the support equipment into the magnet area.

7.4.4 Safety

One of the great attractions of MRI is that it avoids the use of ionising radiation. The absence of ionising radiation, however, has not blinded the pioneers of the technique to the possibility that MRI may present other hazards. Apart from the obvious hazards common to all technical equipment – electric shock, or falling off the patient couch – and the potential toxicity of contrast agents, it is necessary to consider three which are inherent to the MRI technique itself: the radiofrequency used for pulses, the static magnetic fields, and changing magnetic field gradients.

Radiofrequencies. The main measurable effect of the energy absorbed by the body from an applied radiofrequency radiation is a small rise in body temperature. Different tissues absorb energy with differing efficiency, so the heating effect itself must be limited rather than the RF power applied. Current safety regulations specify a temperature rise of less than 1°C in the whole body or in any mass of tissue exceeding 1 gram. This corresponds to a specific absorption rate (SAR) of less than 0.4 watts per kg over the whole body, or less than 2 watts per kg over a small mass.

Static fields. Apart from the mechanical effects on ferromagnetic objects mentioned above, there seem to be no measurable harmful effects on humans from static fields of up to 2 tesla. Even at much higher fields, the only reported effect seems to be dizziness induced by the effect of the field on fluid in the semicircular canals. In theory, blood flow will interact with strong fields, as will nerve conduction, but these seem not to have any effect in practice so that static fields of the type used for MRI appear to present no hazard to health.

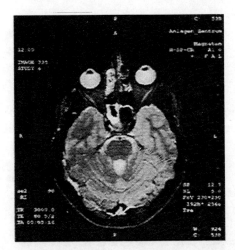

Transverse section of head. (Image courtesy of Siemens plc Medical Engineering)

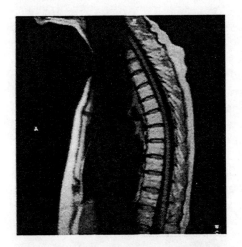

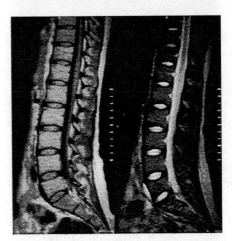

Images of spine. Lower images show two different contrast regimes. (Images courtesy of Siemens plc Medical Engineering)

Changing magnetic fields. The first detectable effect of changing magnetic fields is the production of *magnetophosphenes* – light flashes in the eyes. These appear at rates of change around 2 tesla/second and are not regarded as harmful. Rapid and large changes in magnetic field, in excess of 60 tesla/second, have been reported by volunteers to cause tingling or even pain, but again without any apparent damage: such changes are in excess of any likely to be used in MRI applications.

The conclusion from many studies and from the experience of hundreds of thousands of patients is that MRI is a safe technique and may be applied to almost all patients, excepting only those with ferromagnetic implants and certain types of pacemaker.

7.5 Areas of clinical application

MRI is superior to computed tomography (CT) and to ultrasound imaging in a number of important applications. This superiority stems partly from its ability to differentiate soft tissues, and more particularly from the weighting of contrast by T_1, T_2, proton density or contrast agents which provides the operator with greater freedom in tuning the image for the desired diagnostic purpose. On the other hand, the time taken to acquire an image means that it is easiest to image parts of the body that can readily be kept stationary. As an example, conventional MRI imaging of the thorax can be difficult unless data collection can be triggered by the motion of the heart or chest. In consequence, a number of clinical applications are now considered to be particularly appropriate for MRI.

Brain. The high resolution and good tissue differentiation of MRI make it important in the diagnosis (or, of course, exclusion) of intracranial tumours and various problems with blood vessels, as well as the assessment of trauma damage and haematoma. Conditions such as multiple sclerosis that cause demyelination can also be confirmed using MRI.

Spine, Head and Neck. MRI is particularly good for imaging the spinal cord and intervertebral discs, showing degeneration, damage or congenital malformation. For imaging of the head a particular advantage is that slice direction is controllable, so that coronal sections may be viewed in a way not really possible with CT enabling problems with such structures as the eye sockets to be investigated.

Musculoskeletal. Although fibrous cartilages and ligaments do not give proton signals, they may be mapped via signals from the surrounding tissues. In consequence the degree of detail available in visualising shoulder, elbow, wrist, knee and ankle joints exceeds that of any other non-invasive technique.

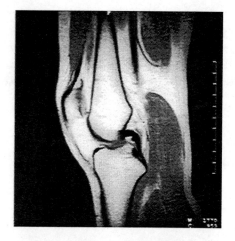

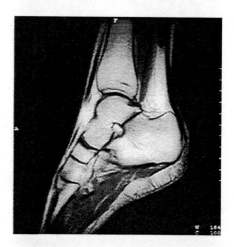

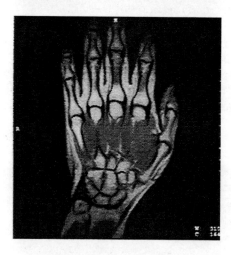

MRI images of joints. (Images courtesy of Siemens plc Medical Engineering)

Pelvis. Tumours of the pelvic region, especially of the bladder, uterus and scrotum, may be visualised by MRI. Although the safe nature of MRI would seem to suggest its use in prenatal imaging, in practice the movement of the foetus prevents successful applications in this area.

Cardiovascular imaging. The potential for detailed soft-tissue images, along with the detection and measurement of flow, would seem to make MRI essential for imaging the heart. The radiofrequency pulses may be gated so that images are always taken at the same stage of the cardiac cycle, although this is difficult when the beat is irregular so that further developments may need to await more general availability of fast imaging methods (next section).

Flow measurement and angiography. Blood vessels often appear as bright spots in normal images, because the flow of blood introduces spin systems of a different phase into the detection slice. A map of phase may be used as an indication of the flow rate, and diffuse flow may also be measured. These observations lead to further applications in diagnosis. Most current methods of conventional angiography (imaging of blood vessels) rely on the injection of radio-opaque or nuclear contrast agents, an invasive procedure not without its hazards. MRI offers the possibility of mapping flow in a variety of ways: for example a small volume of blood whose protons have been excited in a slice-selection process can act as a bolus of labelled spins whose progress can be monitored. Flow rates can be measured, and laminar and turbulent flow distinguished. Appropriate pulse sequences permit imaging of flow both parallel and perpendicular to the image plane, and difference imaging can suppress the image of surrounding tissue to give angiographic images similar to those from conventional radiography (see opposite). More general availability of these procedures, as with all medical imaging methods, will depend as much on their cost-competitiveness with existing techniques as on any other perceived advantages.

Functional Imaging. A very exciting new prospect is that of functional imaging, particularly the study of brain function using MRI. Stimulation of a region of the brain, for example by a visual stimulus, causes a change in the flow of blood to that region. This change can be monitored either by using GdDTPA contrast agent, or by making use of the fact that the magnetic properties of oxygenated and deoxygenated haemoglobins differ, and that this difference is reflected in the T_1 of the image. Hence T_1-weighted difference spectra taken in the presence and absence of a stimulus reveal the region of the brain which is being stimulated. The technique holds out considerable promise in the investigation of brain function.

(a) Readout gradient is regularly reversed to induce successive gradient echoes

(b) Blips of frequency-labelling gradient incrementally phase-encode spins, "scanning" image in gradient direction

(c) Succession of echoes (up to 256) sample image space: largest echo at time TE after initial pulse

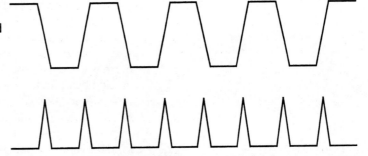
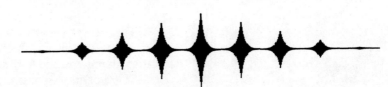

Schematic of the data-collection phase of echo-planar imaging— see below.

7.6 Images in a flash – echo-planar imaging

An MRI angiogram of blood vessels in the brain (see opposite). (Image courtesy of Siemens plc Medical Engineering)

One of the major problems of conventional MRI is the time needed to collect the data for an image. Given that the repeat time TR ranges from 0.5 to 2 seconds, and that frequently 256 sets of data are acquired, each image can take up to ten minutes after all the setting-up procedures have been followed. This can be a serious drawback, both in terms of imaging for patients who find it difficult to keep still, and in terms of the throughput of patients and hence the cost-effectiveness of the technique. The dominating factor in determining TR is the need to allow time for substantial longitudinal relaxation following the initial 90° pulse. It is possible to reduce this time substantially by using the gradient-echo method with a very small flip angle: total acquisition time can be reduced to a few seconds at some cost in the signal-to-noise quality of the image, which is T_1 weighted under these conditions. Operators frequently use such imaging regimes for setting up field of view and slice thickness prior to a longer experiment, but image quality is rarely good enough for diagnostic purposes.

A fast-image method of much greater potential is the *echo-planar imaging* (EPI) method associated with the name of Peter Mansfield. This is a way of collecting all the data for a whole image from a single excitation. The initial slice-selection is essentially the same as for conventional imaging methods, and other pulses and gradients may be applied as usual to set up a spin-echo or to condition the spins for particular purposes: the main novelty comes in the acquisition stage. Instead of keeping a readout gradient constant as in conventional imaging, a strong readout gradient is successively reversed, each time producing a fresh gradient-echo. In order to differentiate these echoes for the data-processing stage, they are phase-encoded by applying a controlled blip of frequency-labelling gradient in between echoes. The largest echo occurs at a time TE after the original pulse, and data can be collected until T_2 relaxation has reduced the magnetisation too far for effective detection. In this way an image can be acquired very fast indeed: less than 100 ms is normal so that, for example, real-time movies may be made of a beating heart. In addition, the operator can vary the parameters of observation (T_1 and T_2 weighting, for example) while observing the results of changes instantly rather than at the end of 5-10 minutes acquisition. This can be very important, because it is quite possible for the T_1 and T_2 changes brought about by disease in a particular tissue to cancel out, so that a careful exploration of both is essential.

EPI makes very heavy demands on instrumentation: Very fast data handling and display, highly homogeneous static fields, and most importantly the ability to switch strong (10-40 millitesla per metre) field gradients very fast, with rise times of the order of 100 msec and repetition at up to 2000 Hz, all point to expensive leading-edge technology. However, the advantages are such that it is likely that EPI will become much more common in the next few years.

7.7 NMR microscopy and the limits of resolution

A medical imaging spectrometer has a magnet bore of perhaps 100 cm and an effective field of view in the range 20-60 cm square for its 256 x 256 pixel final image. An obvious development might be towards imaging smaller objects at higher resolution - why not use MRI with a field of view of, say, one centimetre, or one millimetre, or even less? High-resolution NMR microscopy would be a unique way of observing the fine detail of the soft tissues of an organism, just as medical MRI does on a coarser scale. To an extent, this dream may be realised: the best resolution currently achieved lies in the range 10-100 µm. To form micro-images like this, with fields of view between 0.1-2.5 cm, a formidable list of technical problems needs to be overcome.

7.7.1 Factors controlling spatial resolution:

(a) *Signal-to-noise.* The principles of NMR microscopy are identical to those of normal MRI: signal is collected from individual voxels whose position in space is coded by magnetic field gradients. However, the signal obtainable from a single voxel is proportional to its volume. If you halve the linear dimensions of a voxel its volume goes down by a factor of eight and so does the signal obtainable from it. One-eighth the signal requires sixty-four times as many pulse-collection cycles to provide equivalent signal-to-noise ratio, so we may conclude that high-resolution images will require long accumulation times. To some extent the problem may be mitigated by working at high static magnetic fields: measure-

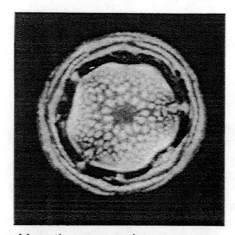

Magnetic resonance microscopy - cross-section of asparagus stem, pixels 70 µm square, slice thickness 200µm. (Image by courtesy of Bruker Spectrospin Ltd.)

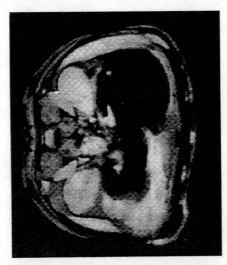

Magnetic resonance microscopy - cross-section from the abdomen of a living rat. (Image by courtesy of Bruker Spectrospin Ltd.)

ment time varies with $1/B_o^3$, so doubling the field reduces accumulation time by a factor of eight. It is much easier to produce uniform high fields with the small-bore magnets used for microscopy.

(b) *Linewidth.* The linewidth of all NMR resonances is inversely proportional to T_2, the transverse relaxation time. For water in living tissue, T_2 will normally be in the range 50-500 msec, giving a linewidth of several Hz. Now for protons, the Larmor frequency varies with magnetic field as 42.5 kHz per tesla, so in a typical MRI field gradient of 5 millitesla per metre, the frequency variation will be about 212 Hz per metre of specimen, or about 2Hz per millimetre. Clearly water with a linewidth of, say, 5Hz will overlap several 1 mm pixels in this field gradient. To overcome the problem, we will need to use a stronger field gradient, and the shorter T_2, the stronger the gradient must be. If T_2 is 10 msec, the gradient must be 75 millitesla per metre for a 10 μm spatial resolution - a gradient 15 times as strong as that used for medical MRI. Even stronger gradients will be needed for imaging in solids, where very short T_2 values lead to linewidths in the kHz range.

(c) *Chemical shifts.* Just as with MRI, proton signals other than those from water and having a different chemical shift will produce images displaced from the water image; the effect is overcome by using frequency-selective initial pulses.

(d) *The static and gradient magnetic fields.* Clearly precise imaging is very dependent on homogenous B_o fields and uniform gradients. The best way to overcome residual inhomogeneities in B_o is to use spin-echo imaging which refocuses the dephasing caused by variations in B_o: the disadvantage of this when compared to gradient-echo methods is that the spin-system must be allowed to come to thermal equilibrium (full longitudinal relaxation) before the next pulse is applied, so that spin-echo imaging is slower than gradient-echo.

7.7.2 *Applications of NMR microscopy*

Although NMR imaging does not provide such high resolution as conventional optical or electron microscopy, it does provide detailed images with a resolution down to ca.10 μm in-vivo. It is thus of particular value for such applications as imaging experimental animals (particularly mice), for insects, biopsy samples, plant stems and roots (where flow measurements can be particularly valuable) and on large single cells and embryo development. It also finds a number of applications in materials science, particularly for analysing the diffusion of liquids into solids and for examining the internal structures of polymeric solids, including bone and teeth.

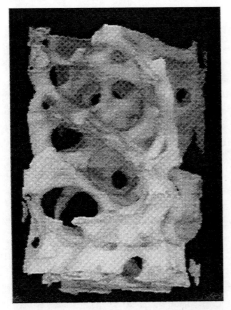

3D structure of a piece of excised bone (4 mm x 2 mm x 2 mm) at a resolution of 35μm, from a study of osteoporosis. (Image by courtesy of Bruker Spectrospin Ltd.)

7.8 MRS – in-vivo NMR spectroscopy

The production of an NMR *spectrum* from a specified region of a tissue or organ holds out interesting prospects for diagnosis. Proton, carbon-13 and phosphorus spectra can all be obtained in vivo, though in practice, most clinical work has been done on ^{31}P resonance with the aim of identifying metabolites and measuring their relative concentrations. It is also possible to measure intracellular pH from the chemical shift of inorganic phosphate, and such measurements can detect metabolic abnormalities such as exercise-intolerance or the effects of oxygen starvation in newborn infants.

7.8.1 Technical problems

Just as with high-resolution solution NMR, high fields are advantageous for spreading out resonances, so high-field magnets are required for MRS. The major problem is to define the region from which the spectrum is obtained. Much MRS has been carried out in homogeneous magnetic fields using surface coils, wound as flat spirals (diagram p.115) which can be placed close to the skin at the region of interest, so that signal is obtained from tissue close to the surface and within the volume excited by the radiofrequency in the coil. Since the technique depends so critically on the efficiency and field distribution of the coil, surface coils are specially designed for different regions of the body. Clearly this method is of most use for tissues, such as brain or skeletal muscle, which offer large volumes near the body surface; it is no longer used in isolation from other localisation methods.

For studies of more deeply located tissues, one method of localisation – topical NMR, or TMR – is to introduce controlled static gradients within the field such that within a particular region at the centre of the magnet the field is homogeneous – so that chemical shifts can be detected – and everywhere else the field strength varies rapidly and is so far off resonance that signals are undetectable, or at least so broad that they can be removed from the spectrum by data manipulation. A reasonable approximation to such a region of constant field can be obtained by combining and opposing different orders of field gradient: homogeneity is adjusted using signals from free water in the patient. The boundaries of a constant-field region are not very well defined, and it is never possible with this method to define an exactly-shaped region; further, it is not possible to move the region selected, so changes in the volume to be scanned must be achieved by moving the patient. Once a region of constant field has been established, a spectrum will be obtained from that part of it which is excited by the radiofrequency pulse from the RF coil: since RF field strength dies away with distance from the coil, coil shape and positioning are also critical to selecting the experimental volume. Signals are obtained from the region where homogeneous magnetic field and strong RF field overlap.

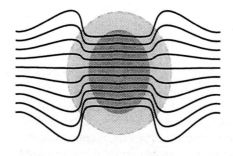

Magnetic lines of force illustrating a region of constant field as used in TMR. Sharp signals are obtained from the strongly-shaded region.

More recently, a variety of techniques have been developed which use imaging-type field gradients in association with selective pulses. The simplest of these is DRESS, (Depth REsolved Surface-coil Spectroscopy) in which a slice is selected just as in imaging methods, and the sensitive volume is defined by the region of overlap between the excited slice and the RF field of a surface coil. More sophisticated are methods of the ISIS type, in which mutually perpendicular slices are excited in quick succession, each by a combination of selective and non-selective pulses, followed by appropriate additions and subtractions of the resulting FID's. In ISIS[†] (Image-Selected In-vivo Spectroscopy) each slice is selected by first collecting data from a single non-selective 90° pulse which gives signal from the whole volume, and then subtracting from this the result of a slice-selective 180° pulse followed by a non-selective 90° pulse. In the second set of data the spins in the slice have received a total of 270° flip, while the spins from the rest of the volume have received only 90°: the subtraction then gives signal only from the slice. A complete set of eight pulses in the presence of x, y and z gradients as shown at left will produce a spectrum from the volume defined by the region of overlap of the three slices.

scan	gradient x	y	z	add/subtract
1				+
2	✓			–
3		✓		–
4			✓	–
5	✓	✓		+
6	✓		✓	+
7		✓	✓	+
8	✓	✓	✓	–

The eight-scan ISIS cycle.

Fourier techniques for MRS spectroscopy involve z-direction slice selection, followed by phase-encoding in both x and y directions, followed by data collection in a uniform field so that the FID can be processed in the usual way. Such methods give separate spectra from each voxel, but of course the double phase-encoding step means that data collection times are inevitably high: however, one major advantage of having a separate spectrum from each voxel is that metabolite maps may be constructed, showing the intensity of each resonance as a function of position on the slice. These metabolic maps may be overlaid on a conventional image of the slice to relate spectroscopic features to anatomical detail. The resolution of such maps compares with that of positron emission tomography (PET) images.

Given effective location, the other major problem for MRS is the relatively low concentration of NMR-sensitive nuclear species – except water protons – in living tissue. This restricts spectroscopy to those compounds which are present in reasonably high concentrations. Proton spectra may be obtained in 10 minutes from compounds present at around 1mM in a volume of perhaps 10 ml, phosphorus at about 1 mM in 30-50 ml will take 20 minutes, while natural-abundance carbon-13 spectra can be obtained in 30 minutes from larger volumes, but only if the compound containing them is present at 20 mM or more. Clearly higher concentrations or larger volumes will produce spectra more quickly: much MRS spectroscopy is performed on large-volume organs such as brain, liver or major muscles.

† Ordidge, R.J., Connelly, A., Lohmann, J., *J.Magn.Res.* 66 283-294 (1986)

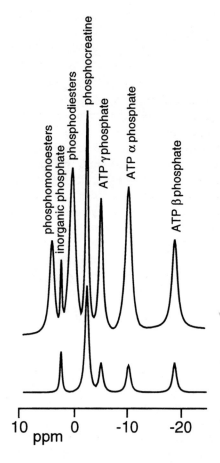

Phosphorus resonances obtainable from metabolites in brain (top spectrum) and muscle (bottom spectrum).

7.8.2 *In-vivo spectra*

The most commonly employed nuclei for clinical in-vivo spectroscopy are protons and phosphorus, with carbon-13 mostly limited to research applications by its long data-acquisition times. In each case, signals can be assigned to dominant metabolites present in the tissue being examined. As an example, the phosphorus spectra illustrated at left contain resonances from creatine phosphate, phosphomono- and di-esters, the three phosphates of ATP and intracellular inorganic phosphate. Inorganic phosphate in intracellular solutions has a pKa of about 6.7-6.8, and its two ionic forms have different chemical shifts: rapid equilibrium between the two forms near the pKa means that a single resonance is visible, and its chemical shift is a measure of intracellular pH. Thus it is possible to measure, for example, the change in pH as lactic acid builds up in muscle tissue during exercise, and the rate of recovery.

Much useful information can also be gained from comparisons of metabolite levels: an important application of such measurements is in the monitoring of brain metabolism in newborn babies. The ratio of the intensities of signals from phosphocreatine and inorganic phosphate is a good indicator of the status of brain metabolism: a low phosphocreatine resonance can be an early indication of metabolic disturbances due to hypoxia or cerebral haemorrhage, or indeed arising from inborn errors of metabolism. The non-invasive nature of the MRS technique makes it particularly valuable for this delicate but urgent diagnosis. Metabolite levels can also be used in studies of muscle, either to monitor the effects of exercise on normal or diseased muscle, or to assist in the diagnosis of disease such as Duchenne muscular dystrophy. As with every aspect of NMR mentioned in this and earlier chapters of this book, an enormous amount of productive work is being carried out in this area, and new techniques appear almost daily. NMR was once tagged "the technique with the eternally rosy future": it seems that the future has now arrived, and that the prophecy was correct.

Select Bibliography

The point of a primer is that it is just a beginning – the first book of many. In the preceding pages we have only skimmed the surface of a vast subject. The books listed below, just a few of hundreds which are available, will broaden and deepen your new understanding of NMR and its applications in the life sciences: you will certainly need them if you intend to use NMR in your own research work. The first three in particular are worth owning if you are going to be seriously engaged in their subject areas.

S.W.Homans (1992) *A Dictionary of Concepts in NMR* Oxford University Press
An essential reference: more an encyclopaedia than a dictionary, a series of clearly-written and extensively cross-referenced articles cover all the main ideas and instrumental techniques in high-resolution NMR. Also provides a fairly gentle introduction to the more mathematical treatment of NMR phenomena.

G.C.K.Roberts (Ed.)(1993) *NMR of Macromolecules: A Practical Approach* IRL Press
Another essential source of detailed and practical information on the structure determination of proteins, nucleic acids and oligosaccharides, from sample preparation to data analysis and computation. Indispensable if you want to use high-resolution NMR yourself.

C.Westbrook and C.Kaut (1993) *MRI in Practice* Blackwell
C.Westbrook (1994) *Handbook of MRI Techniques* Blackwell
Two books offering accessible explanations and practical guidance on the clinical application of MRI, and at a very reasonable price.

A.E.Derome (1987) *Modern NMR Techniques for Chemistry Research* Pergamon
Designed primarily for chemists and a model of clear exposition, this non-mathematical text gives a comprehensive introduction to the complexities of pulse and 2D NMR.

G.M.Clore and A.M.Gronenborn (Eds.)(1993) *NMR of Proteins* Macmillan
A substantial collection of articles from an impeccable source.

L.Berliner and J.Reuben (Eds.) *Biological Magnetic Resonance* Plenum
A series of review volumes (volume 1 published in 1978, volume 12 in 1993) covering a wide range of topics.

R.R.Ernst, G.Bodehausen, A.Wokaun (1987) *Principles of Nuclear Magnetic Resonance in One and Two Dimensions* Oxford University Press
The real mathematical heavyweight. Only to be tackled if you know a hawk from a Hamiltonian operator, but all the fundamental theory is here.

K.Wuthrich (1986) *NMR of Proteins and Nucleic Acids* Wiley, New York
O.Jardetzky and G.C.K.Roberts (1981) *NMR in Molecular Biology* Academic Press
Although somewhat older, these books are important guides to many basic principles.

Index

Author's Note:
"An NMR Primer" is based on lecture notes for a course in biological NMR taken by final-year students of Biomolecular Science and Molecular Biology at the University of Portsmouth since about 1975. This version has been produced on an Apple Macintosh IIsi using Pagemaker 5: text is in 10/12 point Palatino, with Helvetica headings: diagrams were drawn using Canvas 3.0. Final output was to an HP Laserjet 4MP at 600 dpi.